A FARMER'S GUIDE to the BOTTOM LINE

Also by Charles Walters

Holding Action
Angry Testament
Unforgiven
The Case for Eco-Agriculture
Eco-Farm, An Acres U.S.A. Primer
A Life in the Day of an Editor
Raw Materials Economics
Weeds, Control Without Poisons
Fletcher Sims' Compost
Socrates — The Lost Dialogues

Editor

The Albrecht Papers, Volumes I-IV

Co-Author

A Farmer's Guide to Homestead Rights
The Carbon Connection
Mainline Farming for Century 21
The Economics of Convulsion
Hands-On Agronomy
The Carbon Cycle

A Farmer's Guide *to the* Bottom Line

Charles Walters

Acres U.S.A.
Austin, Texas

A Farmer's Guide *to the* Bottom Line

Acres U.S.A., Publishers
P.O. Box 91299
Austin, Texas 78709 U.S.A.
(512) 892-4400 • fax (512) 892-4448
info@acresusa.com • www.acresusa.com

Printed in the United States of America

Publisher's Cataloging-in-Publication

Walters, Charles, 1926-
   A Farmer's Guide to the Bottom Line/Charles Walters
   Austin, TX: ACRES U.S.A. 2002

   xv, 212 p. ill.
   Includes index.

   ISBN: 0-911311-71-8

   1. Farm management — Decision making. 2. Family farms — Management.
3. Home-based businesses. I. Walters, Charles, 1926-   II. Title

        S561.W35   631.1

Dedicated to the memory of Lee Fryer, whose Earth Foods books helped pilot Acres U.S.A. *during its first trying years, and who provided first rate copy when routinely required.*

"If city people only knew how much their final welfare depended on rural and farm prosperity, they'd stand at the farm gate and prevent products of the farm from going into trade channels at prices too low to support continuing farm production."

— Arnold Paulson

Contents

Foreword

Unlike some of the gardening and farming journals, written by penthouse biologists and horticulturists, this guide is a compendium of facts, ideas and results hatched by live people in settings nature has allowed. As used in this book, the term *organic* is opposite artificial, and will not be encumbered by the other nuances of definitions modern science might wish to bestow.

Before the reader can take seriously the premises of the full *Guide*, he or she will be required to dismiss a myth that has crippled not only clean, wholesome and safe food production, but also caused civilization to whimper away its heritage. That myth is known nowadays as the Earl Butz syndrome. This myth holds that size is of absolute necessity not only to accommodate the welfare of the producer, but the nation's food supply as well. The apartment houses of great cities are full of unhappy people who would find a reason for being, and probably a better living, if allowed to operate a farm facility. Yet the ideas of "get bigger or get out" has gained a hammerlock on the thinking of nearly everyone from Department of Agriculture officials to the smallest trivial gardener. Academia, Extension, all the intellectual advisers from 4-H to the farm magazines, idealize the size conceit as though a revelation has just come down the tabernacle aisle.

I discovered this myth while riding with the Australian counterpart of our extension service in the outback just over the Blue Mountains. "Just what is the optimum size farm around here?" I wanted to know. The Australian paused for a moment. "I wish I knew," he said. And then he related how one grower with 20 acres in his administrative area was making a good living, whereas the station we were passing was entering bankruptcy — with "10,000 bloody acres." "Hectares," I corrected. "No, acres, you might say we use the American term to strike a blow for freedom," he said.

It came to me that by any measure except man-hours, smaller operations were more productive, more efficient, and that the rubrics of finance have so ordered the organic universe as to install myth status to the idea of scale at any price.

A myth, if we use the standard dictionary definition, is a traditional account of unknown authority usually with a historical basis, serving to explain some observed phenomenon. It is not difficult to discern the historical basis for this myth.

Most of the world speaks and alludes to the final producer as a peasant who works without much status and with little compensation for a duke or lord of the manor. Political economy was governed by the proposition that food and fiber production be taken from the producer, giving him very little in return. With this surplus of wealth the society could maintain its courts, armies, constabularies, civil servants, priests and entertainers. The idea that some sort of institutional arrangement be constructed to pay the peasant for as much wealth as he produces was then as alien as that of a commoner disagreeing with the "your worship" and "royal highness" people.

The settlement of the American lands introduced a new term, *farmer*. An American farmer was not a peasant, for he was a freeholder. His land was his own. He produced for himself what he wanted and sold the rest to a market he did not set or control.

At the time of the American Revolution the farmer fed himself and only a fraction of another family. By the time of the Civil War, the state of the arts had conferred enough efficiency on the food production system to feed both the farm family and another family engaged in some manufacturing or service enterprise. This efficiency factor, coupled with the movement of some functions off the farm — notably, slaughtering, machinery fabrication, etc. — installed in the American lexicon a mythology that is seldom questioned, much less contested. Today library shelves groan under the weight of well-funded studies that deify the economy of scale and defend the obvious correctness of a public policy that has proscribed the death of the small farm, even the family farm.

Near Corning, Iowa, where I once served the National Farmers Organization (NFO) as an in-house scribe, a small farm provided shelter and tranquility for one of the men in the meat department. We used to pause under the majestic shade trees or near the ponds on the farm, a mere eighty acres. The original owners raised a family of eight on that farm, sending most of them on to higher education. Yet as the NFO battled for higher prices, it seemed self-evident that no one could make a living on so small an acreage. "Something was wrong," we reasoned. One or more of farming's wheels were running off the road in the sand.

I mention these seeming contradictions because they require answers. Clearly, we have compromised the myths that give meaning to our lives, and those who seek a role in agriculture suffer most because of this loss. Implied here is a fact that to me seems self-evident, whether positive or negative, the myth-guided principles that give tone and character to civilization are always grounded in true fact. It is the bent of the myth that makes a profound difference in group outcome.

The movie *How the West Was Won* exhibited better than most the drive of the self-reliant, west-bound pioneers, afraid of nothing, capable of everything endurance, wisdom and fortitude could account for — the kind of myth, in short, we need to cultivate.

The "get bigger or get out" myth has become destructive, as the following few data will illustrate.

Unfortunately, broad spectrum data and econometrics do not serve the farmer-entrepreneur very well. The story has been told — in Homer's *Odyssey* no less — how Odysseus encountered the Cyclops in the cave. This giant's living room was well appointed with the comforts of the times — a larder of food, pens for extra animals, comfort for sleeping, and strong draught for the spirit or the soul. Odysseus and six of his men entered while the one-eyed giant was away, they stayed on to see him return and block the entrance with a seemingly unmovable stone. When Cyclops saw the shipwrecked sailors, he seized two of the men, knocked out their brains and then devoured them, limbs, bones and all. The Cyclops then fell into a deep sleep with impunity. Odysseus and his remaining men could not escape and therefore were in no position to attempt to slay the brutal giant.

A few educated people still read the *Odyssey* of Homer. Fewer still see the connection between parable and life. Those who hope to escape the harmful myths that govern our lives will not do well under the spell of the modern Cyclops, the TV set. As with Homer's Cyclops, it first knocks out the brains before it devours the rest of the civilized man.

This manual necessarily starts with how to let go of harmful myths, especially those perpetuated by the several republics of learning, and the media put-downs that countermand uncommon good sense. The impulse to make a decent living in a soul satisfying profession is always energized by thought, intensive desire, focus, and a logical checklist. But, always, "In the beginning . . . the word."

This much said, you may well wonder where are we on the curve of history? The recorded demise of farming as a favored life style clashes in the minds of many with the following observation: in fact, the rules today are the same for entry into any successful business — find a need and fill it. Reliance on the traditional concept of creating production because there is always a market belongs to stories that begin with "Once upon a time." The recorded codification of that old world view can be found in the transcripts and court papers of *V.B. Morris, et al, vs. D. Glickman.*

This suit was brought in early 1996 when Congress tested the resolve of several conventional farmers by refusing to pass a new farm bill, the old measure having expired on December 31, 1995. Congressman Pat Roberts, who headed the House Agriculture committee, wanted all farming legislation erased, including the Acts of 1949 and 1938. All that remained of the above listed laws were several reporting requirements. The 1949 Act survived in amended form. This meant that unless it was refurbished before December 31, 1995, basic storable commodities would revert to a 60 to 90 percent of parity formula. The plaintiffs argued that indeed all the amendments had expired, and that therefore bonds had to be issued so that the Commodity Credit Corporation would offer loan rates that would adjust all those storable commodities back to a 60 to 90 percent formula, as decreed by the Secretary of Agriculture. In practical terms this meant that corn might be eight dollars a bushel, wheat on the appropriate scale, soybeans near twice that amount. With commodities going into the loan programs, the trades would have to bid up commodities to the loan level in order to buy them. The cost to the government, if the 1942-1952 period is consulted as a guide, would be zero.

The judge dallied, and under pressure Congress passed the 1996 Act, the so-called Freedom to Farm Act, and set into motion a seven-year countdown for a total exit of government from commodity price maintenance. The complete bankruptcy of that law has since become apparent.

The weary public and probably most of those who read these lines do not understand that agriculture policy, at least since 1949, has canceled out profitable large-scale agriculture for the United States because it is now based on international trade and accommodation of several international grain companies. Anyone who thinks he can produce basic storable commodities for international prices is at least several bricks shy of a load.

But America still has an ample share of irrepressible individuals. Look around you and special businesses pop into view. One and all they find a need and fill it. There is no greater need today than food produced without reference to toxic genetic chemicals. It is not necessary to detain the rest of this presentation explaining why. The steady transfer of income from food to sickness care has accomplished an adequate explanation.

How, then, is it possible to transfer expenses back from sickness care to proper payment for the only source of good health? The first step is total abandonment of the mythology that has so far emptied the countryside. Once this mind-set adjustment has been made, verbal concern about macro-economics also can be left behind. For this reason the chapters that follow will give very little attention to the grand design that rises from the dismal swamps of the Washington beltway, and concentrate on close to home *how-to* subjects, much as the front title promises.

The departure of public policy from sound economics to special interest subsidies has had its effect over the last five decades, making food producers the villains of the piece and a subject of stand-up comedy. Shortly before the start of Century 21, most small farmers had become an apparition, defined out of existence by figure wranglers astride plush-bottom office chairs. At the time of the Farm Act of 1996, there remained about 314,000 commercial farms in the United States only. Such farms were computed to have earned at least $100,000 in gross sales. To satisfy USDA, these production units also earned more on-farm than off-farm income. To govern these farms, USDA salaried 106,000 bureau people — one for every three full-time farmers. These many bureaucrats are required to administer the several programs hatched by Congress to keep open imports, and at the same time pace the rate of farm bankruptcy.

Jay Leno, David Letterman, and Johnny Carson made nightly comedy routines out of, say, the wool and mohair program "in the interest of national defense." (In the 1950's it was believed, according to the comedians, that we could confuse the Russians by throwing blankets over their heads. While the Ruskie's were pounding each other in the dark, we could reach the missile sectors and blow up the world.) Farmers became the butt of jokes about being paid not to produce hogs, or harvesting subsidized honey ($100 million to about 2,100 beekeepers, $47,000 each.) With nearly 25 percent of farm income as defined by USDA coming from government, it was easy to turn farmers into ogres, people without respect for themselves and a miserable menace to society.

The comedians and the government policy makers blithely went about the business of undercutting the American producer. Prices were regulated down to a world level for basic storable commodities while creating surpluses via the medium of imports — one percent in terms of domestic production being enough to wreck the American price requirement in most cases — then paying out subsidies selectively, in a manner best calculated to lavish disrespect on the farmers.

As with other economic thinkers who have seen the answer to the economic riddle in the laws of energy, we are required at this point to reflect on the position of the farm in the scheme of things.

Here we are, the support mechanism for a civilization in residence on a floating speck in the universe, just as the Sun is the support mechanism for the planet, its life and economies. This Earth is being swung by a gravitational string in a 300 million-mile orbit around its nebular Sun, wobbling slightly on its axis so that on June 21 in say, the Northern Hemisphere, summer arrives, crops ripen and food stock piles are produced. This floating speck, it turns out, is 8,000 miles in diameter, 25,000 miles in circumference, spinning on its axis once every 24 hours, giving each spot its fair and equal quota of daylight and darkness. Water covers 74 percent of this planet, only 26 percent is dry land. Out of this 26 percent, only eight percent constitutes suitable farm land, and three percent can be used to grow row crops.

At the entry to Century 21, some six billion people inhabit planet Earth, almost all of them crowded into bread baskets of the world — half in Asia and the South Pacific, a fourth in Europe and Africa, one-sixth in North and South America. These data are recited here to point out that all is finite, that food production cannot be considered free manna from heaven, that there are limits to everything under the sun. Cropland in the United States holds at approximately 313.5 million acres, a figure that permits little more than an acre per capita for every man, woman and child. Now that Century 21 has arrived, hunger appears to be the world's legacy.

Only by encouraging efficient use of small farms, by making more profitable the small family-sized farms, by decentralizing indirectly to rural areas, by restoring prosperity to rural communities, by reversing big city population flow back to the countryside, and by stimulating the importance of the small farm, can food shortages be delayed and abolished in the United States.

Not mentioned above was the general proposition that subsidies to the consumer by government-bonded indebtedness these many years also has to be reversed. The cutting edge of these many reversals is the subject of this book. For the individual, profit for the farm is devoutly to be wished. For the community at large, profit for the farm is mandatory because the manufacturing and service sectors — government, school teachers, entertainers, clerks and preachers included — cannot be sustained without a prosperous primary production industry.

Lamented Arnold Paulson, an early farm fighter: "If city people only knew how much their final welfare depended on rural and farm prosperity, they'd stand at the farm gate and prevent products of the farm from going into trade channels at prices too low to support continuing farm production."

Not many people have the judgment or maturity it takes to understand Paulson's statement. Nor is their government likely to align its perception of reality with the support system for the exchange economy. Joseph Schumpeter, the Austrian economist, said it was the role of the entrepreneur to destroy the existing economic order by introducing new forms of organization, often canceling out time-honored institutional arrangements. The peddler with his cart under the manor wall was an entrepreneur. He was more despised and looked down upon than any peasant up to his armpits in mud, yet after this cloud, no bigger than the palm of a hand, rolled over, the lord of the manor was done, knight errantry was in shambles, and business enterprises, not kings, proclaimed the future.

If Joseph Schumpeter is correct, the person most likely to destroy America's enchantment with big business is the founder of a new business. By the beginning of Century 21, it became apparent to many in government, perhaps for the first time, that the entrepreneur, not the military-industrial-university complex held the key to job creation. It also became apparent that agriculture's participation in the well-being of the exchange equation depended on a new perception of the raw materials producer's role. Farmers have complained bitterly about the loss of nearly five million farms between the post WWII years and the present. But the dynamics of change have not spared the industrial company or worker either. During the 1980s for instance, *Fortune* 500 firms were laying off workers by the millions — 3.5 million in the 1980s alone. During that decade, in 1988 for example, 3.6 million new jobs were created by small firms, the self-employed and new farmers. During this time frame, half a million smaller firms managed to grow by 20 percent a year.

Even as these lines are written, this means that farmers must abandon the economic, political, and social role they have endured in the past and recast their operations into an enhanced entrepreneurial role. Joseph Schumpeter has provided us with a written definition of an entrepreneur, while at the same time *Fortune* 500 companies continue to extinguish 400,000 jobs a year.

It is not the purpose of this guide to deal with macro-economics, except as indicated in the preview and last chapter of this study. Nor can these lessons hope to gain the attention of what is left of so-called conventional farming, trapped as it is in the dust bin of thinking that has lost its way. Probably no more than 50,000 people will read this book. I cannot guess how many will apply the lessons contained therein, but those who do will gain a great deal of the insight needed to reach a profitable bottom line.

Editor's Note: In 1995, Acres U.S.A. *celebrated its 25th year of publishing. To honor the many eco-farmers we have met and talked with all across America, we selected two model farmers to represent sustainable agriculture in each state. Many of those stories are reprinted here. Successful farming is represented by farms that survive — crops are rotated and some fall away to make room for innovation. Nothing survives without new growth. While some of our model farms may have changed since their stories first crossed the pages of* Acres U.S.A., *the lessons they taught remain as examples of how to achieve a successful bottom line.*

CHAPTER 1

The Farm Dilemma

Some three decades ago, in a now forgotten book entitled *Angry Testament*, I asked a question that may have seemed rhetorical at the time. "What was it about farming that made tilling the soil both a curse and a blessing for mankind?" During the early days of organization in the old NFO we asked ourselves that question, one and all. Even before the new economics had conquered everything in sight, we wanted to know what it was about the farming business that made the primary producers of farm crops easy prey, not only for the eggheaded policy makers, but for the business community as well. Ever since I graduated from Creighton University in Omaha, Nebraska, I wondered why so little had been written about this dilemma. Since World War II, the entire rural community has watched the growth of corporate farming, the development of contract feedlots, the decline of the truly independent family farm, and the attendant economic and social withering of the small rural community. Anyone able to analyze has observed the power of economic and institutional forces to pour acid on the walls of a society that was, always alert to the same nagging question: are these trends inevitable, or are there choices still available to the independent on the farm?

Some parts of what has happened to agriculture over the past half century are the farmer's own fault. Some are not. Certain observations seem inescapable.

Production activities on the farm have been multiplied by bringing electricity and the wider use of power tools to the countryside. Harvest of bins and bushels has been enhanced by the use of pesticides, salt fertilizers and technological advances.

Mechanization, it was believed, caused the average farm to increase in size until commercial farming after WWII required much heavier investment than during earlier decades. Mechanization, coupled with long hours and exploitation of the family's labor, enabled farmers to accomplish more than their industrial counterparts, but low farm prices somehow managed to keep farm income below what it had been during less efficient days.

From a common sense point of view, none of this has added up for anyone who could still make two plus two equal four.

Over the years Extension workers have told farmers to get bigger, to get more efficient, both weapons of choice for agricultural Davids contesting industrial Goliaths. Not one of those educators had the nerve and intellectual honestly to tell farmers they were living in a market dominated by supermarket chains, government bureau people, and policy-writing professors who had encased new economic theories in reinforced concrete.

While farm prices remained stable or went down, retail prices invariably climbed. Not because there was a surplus of commodities, but because the administered price industry had taken its place in the farm as well as the industrial economy. Such industries were powerful enough to shelter themselves from the type of competition usually associated with supply and demand, and could indeed write their own tickets, not only in terms of quality produced, but the volume that could be sold and the prices received.

On millions of farms the signs and realities of the past 50 years appeared much like an ocean change, a force so powerful no one could stand in the way.

For now I will sidestep the uneven places in the road called macro-economics. The last chapter in this book will pick up that tale of woe, but by then the average reader will understand how useless it is to continue farming with business as usual. For now it is enough to point out that traditional farming is subject to high fixed costs and low variable or out-of-pocket expenses, just the opposite of many industrial and commercial activities. Moreover, most of these fixed costs are implicit. The farmer owes himself a wage, he owes himself a return on his investment, and he owes it to himself to build up a depreciation reserve. But if he fails to meet these implicit costs, even if he consumes his capital, he continues to produce. Crops in the soil will continue to grow, and the fatal day of formal bankruptcy is thus delayed. As a result of these tribal norms, the farmer's minimal supply price has the earmarks of being low. The inventory of elements in the farmer's reversed economic equation has made it possible for institutional business and government to maintain a commissary for the nation and at the same time pursue a policy geared to exploiting the farmer, his land and his production. Obviously compliance with the rules set out by the general run of intellectual advisers to the farmer — the "get bigger or get out" down-shouters — have to be rejected, if for no other reason than the observed result of such counselors going

FROM CONVENTIONAL TO ORGANIC

Paul Vidrine, Markle, Indiana, developed an area-specific crop rotation for his 160-acre farm. He is certified organic and grows corn, soy, spelt and buckwheat. When he first bought the place it had been an alfalfa farm and had a lot of problems; weeds were out of hand from so much anaerobic decomposition, and soil compaction was really bad.

By studying and working with the land Paul is now able to grow his crops using rotation, a high-residue cultivator, and cover crops such as rye or clover. The soil holds water now and doesn't wash off in a hard rain. Weeds are not a big problem and beneficials thrive. "We have

more ladybugs than we need," he says, "lots of praying mantis and predatory wasps."

The Vidrine's don't plant anything they don't have a con-

tract for or that they can't take to the elevator in an emergency. Paul explains why he farms organically: "We knew with this size farm we wanted to be organic; you can farm a few acres and do a good job. The product is higher quality. We're not polluting water, not using anything that's nasty toward life. We just think it's a better way to take care of the ground. We eat what we grow and we want to eat good food."

Paul and his family aren't the only ones who want good food. Last year hunters noticed the local deer were full of Paul's blue corn. In addition, Paul says, "There might be a chemical in a bell pepper that would prevent cancer, but if that's not grown right, the element could be missing. They have actually found oranges in grocery stores that have no vitamin C."

In addition to his own business, Paul is involved in the organic movement as a whole. He has served as vice-president and president of the Indiana Organic Crop Improvement Association (OCIA). He also runs Blackstone Organic Consultants to assist farmers transitioning to organic. "We take conventional farmers from step one because more and more organic growers mean a better quality of life."

bankrupt within a year when taking their own advice. "Don't get bigger, get smart," advised an Acres U.S.A. conference speaker named Booker T. Whatley a few years back.

The first plank of traditional farming to be erased is the idea that a farmer can buy supplies at retail and sell production at wholesale. It can't be done without tasting insolvency. While there are only a few ways in which high input costs can be avoided, the goal of selling so as to capture all of the consumer's dollar is attainable. Good records, rapport with friends of your farm, and all the precepts of good business management have as much a place in farming as in any other form of enterprise.

In the pages that follow, I will detail, step by step, many of the secrets of profitable small business management. In this role I will make the point that it is almost impossible to fail if the budding entrepreneur has staying power. I did not set out to operate a farm because my first love was journalism, but as a journalist I realized that I could never publish a line if the support mechanism for the service industry was not kept alive and well. Over the years I have helped many farmers save their land from the hammer with a little book, *A Farmer's Guide to Homestead Rights*. I have files full of correspondence that tell me how farmers have fared because they accepted the precepts of eco-farming as reported in *Acres U.S.A.*

The greatest deterrent to a successful farming venture — as with any business — is having unreal expectations on the one hand, and doubts that the enterprise can succeed on the other hand. The success of *Acres U.S.A.* is well known, and some parts of the story have been related in *A Life in the Day of an Editor*. A similar success story can be read in the book *Fletcher Sims' Compost*. But for my

FIND A NEED

"Find a need and fill it" marched hand-in-hand with the admonition to "get smart" when the 1960s served up a moral crisis for Joe Tooker, Valley Center, California.

Joe Tooker got involved in the natural food movement in the early 1960s. He became interested in the nutritional quality of the foods he ate and sold at natural food stores. It was then he decided to learn more, and enrolled at Emerson College in England where he received a degree in biodynamic farming. From there he worked on biodynamic farms in England and Germany before returning to the states to begin his own organic vegetable farm in southern California. He sold that farm to buy a fruit tree farm in northern California where he is farming today.

Joe grows gala apples, a Japanese persimmon, and feijoa and jujube, which are specialty fruits, on this 47-acre farm. He found the farm in 1988. "It was an old farm but it hadn't been actively farmed in years. It had Class 1 soil and that was a prerequisite of mine. It is much easier to start with good soil, so I have good deep topsoil." The only limiting factor was water, but Joe has dug two wells on the farm that produce 100 gallons a minute, which is enough to drip irrigate his 3,000 fruit trees. His produce is sold directly to store and gourmet restaurants in the Bay area, and his specialty crops go mostly to Asian markets in the area.

Because of his expertise and commitment to sustainable, biodynamic agriculture, Joe has produced tapes and videos on how to do it. In addition, he tries to teach his neighbors about organic farming and proudly notes he "even got one to quit using herbicides."

Joe's commitment to organic farming and teaching organic methods come directly from the revolutionary politics of the 1960s. It is both a personal and political choice for him. The impact his method of farming has on the environment, the nutritional value of the food he produces, the fact that he is not contributing to the further poisoning of the human and animal body, are all as important to him as his farming success.

That success depends on understanding principles, biological and economic, and a bottom line.

purpose two case reports will illustrate how a traffic jam between the ears can be removed to benefit the venture.

Paul Abalos grew up in the poverty of a migrant beet worker's transport or shelter. While still in his mid-teens, he told his parents he wanted to get an education. This was doable because community colleges were available, and hard work often resulted in scholarships being awarded. Paul's dad told him, "Well, you'll have to come in off the road, get a job, and stay put." Paul accepted this advice. He found employment in a restaurant and learned something about the business while observing the tawdry practices that prevailed. In due time he became educated and credentialed for the teacher's craft, but he never quite forgot what really good Mexican food tasted like. The fare generally available north of Austin and San Antonio seemed partial to heavy grease, and perpetrated every bad habit and mistake amateurism is heir to. Paul and his wife found a small abandoned stand, the kind frequently harnessed to selling root beer and soft ice cream. The place had few seats, but there was and always is a need for good food, even in Hereford, Texas, now surrounded by a million head of feedlot cattle. Paul invoked strict discipline in the management of the restaurant known as Les Charro Too. Many locals are convinced the food is the best Mexican west of the Mississippi and east of the river Nile, certainly north of Mexico.

The rule Paul Abalos invoked is absolutely a rule for any enterprise: find a need and fill it. The need has to be filled at a profit, and this can be best achieved by working very close to the vest, controlling and handling expenses without reference to banking connections or consuming inherited capital, two of farming's greatest sins. Over the years Paul Abalos has expanded the food emporium several times, once building an addition himself in order to avoid an increase in rent. Clean, simple, and wholesome became the family's formula, with each plate delivering quality, each perfect for expansion and full employment for the family.

Generally speaking, these requirements fit into any sale, but only two are absolutely mandatory. There has to be a need or a want, and there has to be an ability to pay. Any business operates with this simple formula in mind. Why, then, is agriculture different? Why must farmers sell their products as if on an auction block at a distress sale? Why are costs of production seldom a part of the production-to-consumer sequence? It is not enough to say that agriculture does not have the institutional arrangements required to effect an orderly market, even though this statement is true. For the purpose of this book, I do not intend to set down many of the principles needed to govern farming in any intelligent manner. That role falls under the purview of the intellectual advisers to the food producers.

Here we have to examine what the individual can do, it being accepted that no one holds a gun to the head of a farmer and requires him to sell to the feedlot, the grocery chain, the provender who builds all sorts of exchanges into the grower-to-consumer process. Admittedly, the individual cannot run agriculture, but he or she can get smart, even if some people think the answer is to get bigger.

The individual contemplating the production of poultry, beef, pork, mutton, etc., has this reality to consider. Grains used to feed out livestock are largely in the hands of a few international firms. These firms own a resource most markets cannot comprehend — every grain farmer in the world. They have all the clout it takes to make the market go up or down, and perform either task in a manner best calculated to keep the commodities coming while the land is assembled into a few strong hands. For decades, each morning the Meat Institute sent its yellow sheet suggestions to livestock buyers and by 5:00 A.M. they "discovered" the market prices for the day, and the market almost never relates to the cost of production.

It would seem to be sheer madness to even think of entering such a business, and not many do. Indeed, the producers in the main became established long before the present era, surviving and consolidating, until now almost all of them are extremely vulnerable. But there are values — if that term can be permitted — on the other side of the ledger, and these considerations seem to indicate the approach supported in this *Guide*.

Take poultry. Most broilers are grown in houses that typically handle 40,000 birds. The flocks arrive from hatcheries as one- or two-day-old chicks. Their feed is largely fish meal and so-called bone meal, meaning remains of previous generations of birds and animals. Artificial growth hormones, antibiotics, and anticoccidials to treat fungal infection are the norm. Antibiotics bump up weight gain an additional five percent. These chickens, if they live, are slaughtered in 42 days. Generally, eight crops move through this poultry house assembly line system, delivering to kitchens chickens that have 1,000 percent more fat than their free-roaming organic counterparts of earlier this century.

It is the fat content that most offends human health. There are two types of fat that concern us here: polyunsaturated fats and saturated fats. Unsaturated fats include essential fatty acids. These are essential because they are required for the growth and development of the brain and are components of all cell membranes. They help form hormone-like substances which regulate the immune and vascular systems. Saturated fats author heart disease and unhappy conditions such as breast and colon cancer. The product of the poultry industry may be the worst meat in America, but it has a strong runner up: swine.

Wild pigs were domesticated at some point between the sixth and fifth centuries B.C. At first they were herded, then confined. Today they are kept in a literal strait jacket, like layer hens, and bathed in the ammonia of their own elimination. Some are medicated with a French abortion medicine in order to be kept on a factory birthing schedule. They receive no fresh alfalfa, only a high carbohydrate diet. Wild pigs have twice the concentration of essential fatty acids as saturated fats. The confinement hog has five times more saturated fats than polyunsaturated fats, a transformation ten times the wrong way.

Leviticus prohibited consumption of pork products to the children of Israel because this herbivorous animal had been turned into a carnivore, a scavenger, a competitor for grains, and an animal as unclean as the jackal. It gave residence to and distributed pathogens then, and does the same now in spite of antibiotics and coal-tar derivative medicine.

A second runner-up in the unwholesome meat game is the beef animal. Once a range animal that harvested half the acres — acres man could not harvest or consume — the beef animal grown thereon has been subjected to bovine concentration camps, and the effects on meat protein quality are only now being noted.

The worst case scenario has come to us from England as mad cow disease, or bovine spongiform encephalopathy, TSE, the T standing for "transmissible." The human form is Creutzfeldt-Jakob disease, and it is always fatal. This disease punches microscopic holes in the brain, hence the name *spongiform*. It is transmitted, we believe, by technology that turns herbivores into cannibals. In fact, the Creutzfeldt-Jakob syndrome was first found among South Sea Islanders who practiced cannibalism. Experiments

Bill Welsh (right), his son Gary, and Gary's son Clayton with day-old chickens.

REJECTING TOXICITY

The decision to "have done" with toxic technology often carries with it a severe price tag, as illustrated by the Welsh family vignette.

A bale of hay, a sack of dyfonate and death in the field prompted the Welsh family of Lansing Iowa, to bring down the curtain on 20 years of toxic chemical farming. The trigger mechanism was an empty bag of the above-named pesticide that remained undetected for several months. When the contaminated hay was fed to cows, 40 became sick and 14 died.

That did it. The Welsh family had become disenchanted with low profits and environmental damage in any case. Now the older generation — Bill and Ester Welsh — and the family started looking for production models that did not rely on toxic technology.

They found answers enough to make their 200-plus acres turn a profit. All the crops, it turned out, could be grown without chemicals of organic synthesis, crops being oats, corn, barley, legumes (alfalfa and clover), most for on-farm use.

Gary and Kim now do most of the work, with Dad and Mom Welsh in retirement. Greg Welsh, the only Extension agent in Iowa trained in organiculture, spends the weekends on the Des Moines-area farm, almost always deeply involved in the clean production that has become a Welsh farm hallmark.

The crop nowadays is 50,000 chickens that range out from their pole barn quarters, some 25 slaughter steers and 600 finished hogs, all raised according to eco-friendly methodology.

have revealed that the infecting agent can survive irradiation, x-rays, chemical sterilization, and autoclaving at 360 degrees centigrade for one hour. The agent can persist for years in the soil. Scientists have traced TSE to so-called cattlecake concentrate, bonemeal, or APF (animal protein factor), and other euphemistically-named feed concoctions made from rendering plant meat, including sheep, dogs, etc.

These euphemisms mean that deceased cows, dogs, sheep, whatever, are reduced to mush, bones and all, in rendering plants. Hair, bones, hides, entrails and other contents are hydrolyzed and squeezed into feed chunks for integration with some grain components for the bovine feed. Even though backgrounded on wheat pasture, such animals do not constitute a wholesome diet.

Creutzfeldt-Jakob disease has jumped to Canada, Europe and sites still undisclosed probably because of organophosphate contamination. Although England has put a ban on APF, the issue is still in the debate stage in the U.S. This general disease has now been transmitted to the pig, an animal closely akin to man physiologically.

Quite recently the cow has figured in still another shock wave. Bovine growth hormone, bGH, has been rejected by consumers, yet the industry insists on having the contaminant in milk. Cows are injected with the bovine somatropin hormone every eight days in order to force greater milk production. Some of the hormone ends up in the milk, and as hormone-inoculated cows start to fail, they become canners and cutters for the junk food trade.

This inventory of information contains its own suggestion. Animal agriculture is an important foundation stone for the income side of the national equation. It is being endangered by the technological trap into which it has fallen.

Increasing multitudes see these production technologies as monuments to the stupidity of man, and a disgrace to a civilized society. They see commercial protein meat as unfit for human consumption, and, in increasing numbers, they are turning to the vegetarian way of life or they seek out the ever-increasing suppliers of organic meat.

For now it is enough to observe that the failure of the meat protein industry to supply a fresh, wholesome food product will lead to diminished industry for two reasons.

1. Consumer demand will vanish perceptibly as buyers reject the product — perhaps only a percent a year at a time — either because they are no longer satisfied with tasteless, grease-laden, health-destroying fare, or because they do not have the ability to buy.

2. The ability to buy, I have pointed out, is governed by the ability of the private enterprise sector to pay wages once the credit device fails.

Still, some few are aware of the fact that Creutzfeldt-Jacob disease is virtually indistinguishable from Alzheimer's disease and are willing to shun chain store meats if other suppliers are available.

When grain prices double long enough to cut beef prices in half, even slow absorbers of hard reality realize they cannot break the giants, at least not by playing their game. And yet the astute farmer, acting as an individual, can penetrate the downward curve and find a profit. The desire, need, and ability to pay has now been buttressed by a willingness to spend more on food in order to demolish down-line medical expenses.

While visiting Fletcher Sims near Canyon, Texas, I met a young farmer, Chris Weick, who came to an appropriate conclusion a few years back. He discovered some willing customers in his environment, which included the nearby city of Amarillo. Some 500 customers were willing and ready to make out order forms for fulfillment on one of two days that the farm was open for customer visits each month. Chickens offered were free-roaming, grass- and grain-fed. Porkers dined on legumes and herbivorous foliage, and cows for the beef pool didn't endure the unnatural conditions that have made the landscape for several counties around Amarillo and Hereford an obscenity as well as a stink sink.

As with most farmers, this young fellow grew into his equation quite naturally. He and the German farming heritage from which he descended have always slaughtered on the farm.

Nowadays, because of laws, red meat slaughter is accomplished at USDA approved abattoirs. Most free-range chicken operations are home-based businesses all the way.

Weick has departed the organic production scene because even start-up farmer-entrepreneurs are not excempt from the laws of nature, life, business and economics.

This *Guide* cannot suggest a defined model for all the possibilities attending the growth of the clean food trade. Normally I counsel against spending too much time chasing loans and grants, and yet Diana and Gary Endicott prove that all generalizations are false. With landscaping and teaching experience under their belt, the Endicotts returned to the Bronson, Kansas, Endicott family farm. They tiptoed into rotational grazing, greenhouse production and catch-as-catch-can sales. Then Diana's natural spark started flaming into action. She convinced the Kansas City-based Hen House chain that Rainbow Farm could keep a steady supply of natural products coming — red meat, vegetables — not last, tasty tomatoes.

Since the opener of a few years earlier, the farm's venture and adventure has led the couple to become farmer-entrepreneurs, prize-winning innovators in merchandising, and leaders in helping fellow farmers stay on the farm.

The farmers that use the Rainbow conduit for meat protein products — chickens, hogs, cattle — into some 15 Hen House stores are counted as a co-op with at least 20 farm members. The chickens are free range, as are the eggs. Pork is pastured and natural.

To enlarge the Rainbow Farm plan, Diana convinced Hen House to support the program with ads and in-store promotions, all-natural and chemical-free being the lure.

When the available processing plant burned down, Diana wrote grant proposals and sought and got Kansas agency support for seed capitalization to re-establish the small processing facility's steady traffic that a metropolitan market required. With heads-up innovation and organization, some 20 farmers have been kept on the farm and the future "has never been brighter," even if it looks dismal for the average commodity farmer.

The small co-op is gaining attention nationally. By e-mail, one-on-one demonstrations, word-of-mouth, feature stories, the word has gone out that clean, wholesome food is on the way, in fact here. Here, beef came first. For many farmers, the opener is poultry.

Some growers, Joel Salatin of Virginia for instance, use moveable cages in their chick to chicken sequence, but this won't work on the high plains. Panhandle winds send such cages skittering across the fields like squared tumbleweed. Although sheltered by larger buildings and boarder walls, the best — layers as well as pullets — are free roaming. They all seem to have the sense to come inside to avoid the coyotes.

Chicken slaughter is performed on-farm with small scale equipment, in most cases. Scalding and feather removal take place in ultra-sanitary conditions, as does evisceration. At no time are slaughtered birds subjected to the fecal soup one might find in so-called commercial pluckeries.

"It's a business. I want the consumer's dollar, all of it, and I want a profit based on cost of production," says Jack Graves of Buckner, Missouri.

Because the 450 acres produce most of the grain — a little soybean meal excepted — and because he has left off with the foolish idea of growing grain for the international commodity traders, Chris now has a profitable bottom line.

Whether it is a restaurant at the final end of the food chain, or a farm operator making the best living he's ever made, a number of principles emerge from the above experiences. The motive here is to mine those lessons, refine and extend them, and serve up a guide of maximum value to those still on the farms, or those who have access to farm acres.

There are intelligent people who could help straighten out agriculture, but they do not have the job. It therefore remains for the individual to position the farm for a profitable bottom line. That priority has to start with the farm itself.

CHAPTER 2

Self-Reliance

My dad was a Kansas wheat farmer. He failed to survive the 17 cent wheat of the Hoover era and the Southwestern Kansas Dust Bowl of the 1930s. But out of that experience came the lessons forever etched in my memory. The first, of course, was that no American producer could play the international trade game. In far off Russia, from which so many of those Volga German farmers had fled, Stalin confiscated farms and wheat stocks. The farms were collectivized (which brought on starvation) and the wheat was dumped into international trade channels. At Ness City, Kansas, wheat loaded out on the elevator siding at 17 to 20 cents a bushel. Such a price would not pay land taxes, or even the interest on mortgaged machinery or acres. Thousands of farmers went belly up.

At school, kids dropped out when prices failed to improve, and car caravans started west and east, *Grapes of Wrath*-style. Children in school blamed Roosevelt and recited doggerel of unknown origin.

> *I curtailed crops when I felt mean,*
> *And imported corn from the Argentine.*
> *And when I wanted to punish the folks, you know,*
> *I put my wife on the radio.*

The second great lesson that emerged from the Great Depression was that few could foresee downturns in economic and political events. At regular and irregular turning points, the bankers seemed to take the wealth from those who produced it. At times they even stripped home-canned goods from storm shelter shelves, having already confiscated assets such as buildings, fixtures, machinery and land.

A BREAK WITH THE PAST

The break with a toxic tradition did not come easily for Francis and Ruth Polifka, veteran wheat farmers from near Hays, Kansas. For one thing, Dad Polifka accepted everything the university had to say as Holy Writ, and so far — meaning a decade or more ago — the worst effects of toxic technology hadn't visited its terrible scars on this the greatest wheat belt of the world.

Nevertheless, Frank and Ruth broke with what passes for tradition in modern agriculture, split off their acreage and farmed according to the precepts of eco-agriculture. This has meant trial and error, free-roaming chicken flocks, and buffalo for red meat.

The high plains are dryland country, even though irrigation has invaded the scene. Anhydrous ammonia has burned up precious organic matter over the last decade or more, and this has prompted Polifka to enter composting in a big way. He harvests manure from area feedlots for raw material, he uses billions of unpaid microbial workers to rescue acres, both his own and thousands of acres in wheat production. This role model farmer has proved his ability to harvest more bins and bushels than his chemical counterparts, he has also enhanced quality as well. Hay from clean acres feeds out healthy critters.

Frank and Ruth Polifka grow out some 100 beef cattle and a few buffalo, but the mainstay of this western Kansas farm is wheat, 500 acres, and pasture, about 3,000 acres. Milo and silage round out this model farm package.

Frank spreads 1,200 acres of compost in any one year, and perhaps double that amount.

Ruth's eco-garden is a pleasant oasis, replete with the sound of music — "sound and nutrients," she says — pyramid energy, a strawberry ring in a mammoth tractor tire and the miscellany that farm wife ingenuity can account for.

In his spare time, Frank invents ecology-friendly devices, such as his air-powered glass and eggshell grinder. Withal, the key to topsoil preservation is compost, home stirred and spread.

With a break with the past secure, the Polifka's square production reality with a necessary bottom line. Compost sales and refinement of the pneumatic grinder for processing egg shells big time are a reality. Grain and red meat invite the same bottom line without awaiting a correction in public policy.

The banker sits down at your dinner table three times a day, seven days a week, and takes the first helping. "No amount of money is too small for a banker to go after or steal," was the solemn pronouncement of a kinsman.

Through it all, Dad's dictum had its theme as I grew up. "Capitalize on savings, expand on earnings."

In truth there is seldom enough profit in any enterprise to pay outside carrying costs. That is why the most successful biologically-correct farmers carefully avoid the debt trap. It is true, some eco-farmers borrow on a short term basis, and if all goes well they extradite themselves from a carefully baited trap.

In many cases capitalization is available, yet squandered because steps are not taken to prevent transfer upon death. When the older generation passes, the will is opened and read, and before long the "partner" arrives for his share.

The partner is the Internal Revenue Service. In words suitable to a Charles Dickens novel, a lawyer intones a federal codicil. Because of capital gains and death taxes, the land must be sold. Sometimes a whimpering son-in-law wants his bride's share "right now," or no clear direction has been established for the farm's operation into the next century. Perhaps the son has left for a prodigal adventure because Dad or Grandpa never got around to dealing with the reality of a computerized, tax-heavy, confiscatory government.

None of this is necessary, of course. "Don't sign, sell or walk away" was good advice during distant yesteryears, and it is good advice now. In fact, a simple trust prepared by an expert, can accommodate the wishes of Grandpa, Dad, and son while leaving most estate taxation out in the cold. Once property has been consigned to the proper trust, a trustee and co-trustees administer what is now an artificial person. They can draw from the trust its income, subtract its expenses, and permit co-trustees to draw from the capital accumulation *ad infinitum*. It must have its own IRS number. The trust is immortal. It does not die. It lives on as a going concern unless gutted by failure.

Lawyers and judges may try to penetrate this trust, and they may succeed by luring a participant right into court. Should such a participant honor the summons? The answer is yes, but such disputes at law are not criminal actions. Failure to appear may result in a judgment, but a judgment can be executed only against the individual sued. A defendant who is economically naked is not a good target, even if he is an officer in a trust. The trust, of course, is a secret title holder and cannot be penetrated easily if the farmer has the wits to stay out of court and away from lawyers.

A clear and free piece of ground is generally a necessity for profitable operation. The hand-me-down farm is absolutely the best way to capitalize, with savings dedicated to expansion.

Many frustrated urbanites spend their hours in city apartments reading rural wish books. *Mother Earth News* once loomed large on the scene and for a time *The New Farm*, by the Rodale people, inspired young people to break the chains of monotony and strike a blow for freedom. *Acres U.S.A.*, of course, offers practical how-to information each month.

Unfortunately, a wish does not make it so. Malcolm Beck wished with all his might for a farm, but a background of Texas poverty would not let him borrow money for the purchase. It was just as well. Mere possession of a few acres is not enough. Even the hobby farm requires input money, and expansion from the ground up based on sales alone often does not compute. A better plan has to intervene.

Beck took a job at the railroad switching yard while still a young man, rejecting the advice of many to pursue college training. He figured all education was self education in any case, and he was possessed of enough motivation to pencil out the results and extrapolate (with all the variables in tow) how to arrive at a bottom line. The hobby farm made secure family life. In time Beck used a part of his ample railroad salary to buy a bigger farm. Since he was no stranger to work, he proceeded to compost almost everything available. By now he had rejected most of the Extension advice he'd received, and was going "Rodale organic." As the soil straightened up, his vegetable crops brought San Antonio area people to his outback station, so to speak. There was a lot of money to be made and, added to his switch-yard salary, the living was good for him, his wife and family.

Then one day Malcolm Beck made a profound discovery. A customer had pleaded and begged a few scoops of compost from Beck. Against his uneasy judgment, Beck allowed some of the valued stuff to be carted off. Others made similar demands. It was then that Beck's discovery was made. He could make more money selling compost than he could by putting the compost through orchard and vegetable crops. It was a discovery so profound it changed his life, put Gardenville of San Antonio on the map, and encouraged other young entrepreneurs in Texas to set up Gardenville operations.

Beck will agree that borrowing on a shoestring is too dangerous for instant comprehension. The point here is that Beck started as penniless as most of us. But his career can be summed up in my dad's dictum, "Capitalize on savings, expand on earnings."

Many young families capitalize these eco-farm operations with a second job. Either the wife or the husband can hold down that second job, but much of the cash flow belongs in a savings account.

A little arithmetic can explain why. If you divide the rate of interest on, say, your home loan into 72, the quotient will tell you how many years it takes the interest to double the debt. At 10 percent interest, the interest left unpaid will double the debt in 7.2 years. One out of seven years of your life is a bit much to gift the banker or the insurance company mortgage holder. By doubling the payment during the first years of a mortgage, the amortization schedule is chewed into smithereens. Examine the operation of family finances, and chances are that capitalization can be found, like those legendary acres of diamonds, right underfoot.

I know of two young farmers who entered the business simply by invoking dogged stick-to-it-tiveness. They learned how to repair small engines and slowly inched into the repair business, all while holding down a seasonal IRS job. The time came when they not only purchased the land they wanted, but by that time they also had assembled most of the tools required. Running a small organic farm is no fun if you're constantly strapped for working money. There is never enough working capital if you're feeding the interest mill.

No one can counsel the emerging class of eco-farmers *en masse*. Each case requires its own balance sheet and character profile.

Renting the land seems to go against the grain of start-up farmers. They see someone participating in the fruits of their labor without lifting a shovel. I never have trouble explaining the social side effects of absentee ownership to young people who would like to operate a profitable farm. The idea of the eco-farm is to build up the soil and leave the land in better shape for the next generation. Building up rented land is gifting another the capital accumulation diligent work has accounted for. Nevertheless, it sometimes becomes necessary to rent. The only way to make the appropriate judgment is to scope it out. A realistic budget and *pro forma* income statement sometimes make the stars in the eyes fade away, but it is better to not act in haste for there always follows leisure in which to repent.

Some prospective farmers come to their adventure with unrealistic expectations. Often they are filled with dreams of establishing a self-sufficient operation, a proposition that loses its appeal after only a moment of reflection.

Daniel Boone self-sufficiency simply is not in the cards. To start with, land taxes and the demands of civilization, even for those who do not participate, are too great to be dismissed.

Government agencies are forever ready to pounce upon those who wait to go a different way. That is bad enough. The fact is, the country is now settled, and abundant game is not always a reality. Self-sufficiency know-how is not very available, and when it is, it stops short of the norm most people expect.

I know a clever young man from the Springfield, Missouri area who has a gas, electricity and city water-free home in a wilderness area. His operating costs are near the vanishing point. But his cash income comes from teaching school.

Possibly the biggest unidentified trend in the United States today is the growth of small family farms. These are usually only a few acres in size. Not many people make a living off these acres but their owners — having capitalized with savings — have a great feeling that all is not well with the chain-letter economy sketched out in Chapter 1. They want the security that self-reliance can bestow, and a great many are ready to strike while the iron is hot.

The *situs* is of maximum importance. Except in the west — west of the Topeka, Kansas meridian, that is — and east of the coastal ranges in California, almost everyone lives within or close to medium-range population centers. Anyone with a minimum of land unencumbered by rent or interest lugs, can so arrange crops and income-producing enterprise timely to the demands of the profit and loss expended register.

Preservation of an existing family farm for the next generation is the most overlooked aspect of farm economics. Failure to scope out the metes and bounds of land transfer for the benefit of the next generation ranks only behind government malfeasance as a cause for the elimination of the family farm. Both have contributed to the demise of the bottom line for the farm, loss of the farm itself to "a few strong hands," and elimination of the most successful education facility the nation has ever had — the family farm itself.

During one of my lectures to a small group of National Organization for Raw Materials (NORM) members, I was asked to name the two greatest economists, meaning people who had done the most to explain the buzzing, baffling confusion to the public. My answer was Kathie Lee Gifford and Clark Gable.

Kathie Lee Gifford was the star of a morning television show, and her name recognition inspired business folks to sell her on the proposition of having her own line of clothing for sale at WalMart Stores. One day, she lost her innocence. She learned that her namesake clothes were made in sweatshops that exploited labor and sidestepped most of the cost usually subtracted from the bottom line. In her broadcasts and via her testimony before congressional committee members, she did more to explain the fallacy of free trade than all the professors in North America.

Clark Gable, as the lovable villain in the 1938 movie *Honky Tonk*, conferred a lesson in economics most farmers missed, otherwise they would not have left their farm acres to insurance companies, bankers and the few strong hands so cherished by government bureau people. Candy Johnson, the character Clark Gable portrayed, was shaking down the merchants in a frontier town. Collectors reported back that complaints were getting louder and might invite corrective measures. "Tell them to add it to the cost of the beans," the scoundrel said.

Over the years, farmers have continued to produce, but they have not added their costs to the price of beans. Instead, they have worked for slim or negative wages and consumed their capital.

This business of omitting charges in computing economic traffic has too many farmers leaping to conclusions. Cash traffic is real. Profits are often a product of an accountant's construction. The professional panhandler can taunt a citizen with "You can afford it," to which Candy Johnson would have answered, "So now you're my bookkeeper!"

While working at NFO some 30 years ago, I designed a simple diagram that became a slide and an institutional tool. One component illustrated the usual procedure in determining the price of a product.

```
↑   PRICE TO THE CONSUMER   ↑
            TAXES
     MARKET IN PROCESS COSTS
            WAGES
         CAPITALIZATION
         RAW MATERIALS
```

The second part of the slide explained the usual procedure in agriculture.

```
┌─────────────────────────────────────────────┐
│     PRICE DETERMINED BY OTHERS               │
│            LESS WAGES                        │
│         LESS CAPITAL COSTS                   │
│       LESS OPERATING EXPENSES                │
│   LESS TAXES AND COMPLIANCE COSTS            │
│         LESS SEED, STOCK, ETC.               │
└─────────────────────────────────────────────┘
```

Here the price at wholesale was determined by the trades, and all the arrows ran in the wrong direction.

Especially ignored were interest and tax charges never passed forward in the final sale price. All taxes are a cost of production. This happens to be the least understood fact in American economic life. Candy Johnson knew better, even if Milton Friedman and Henry Hazlett didn't. It is this never-never land instruction that keeps farmers from understanding how taxes impact on the final sales price. Confused and stupefied by academic bug bears, an entire community has been led to believe that raising taxes cools inflated price spirals (the simplistic idea being that a shortage of wallet cash invites bids and higher prices). Some farmers who accept this nonsense actually worry about commodity prices getting too high. They never reason the obvious because academia has made it politically incorrect to consider taxes a part of their bottom line problem.

Actually all taxes, regardless of their target objectives, flow directly into the cost of production whether the shakedown is accomplished by a smiling Candy Johnson, a crooked sheriff, IRS violators of the Constitution, *ad valorem* heist, etc.

Stated simply, all taxes are a cost of production and all taxes are a drain on production. The impact base for all taxes, regardless of how they are levied, is called the Consumer Price Index.

There are a few ways taxes can be evaded. First there is the bald-faced evasion route, which probably earns some assortment of people more than $125 billion a year. A second evasion of taxes is the free-trade route used by expatriate companies to take themselves away from economic conditions with which others must comply. This artifice drains some $250-plus billion from federal, state and local governments each annum.

Some people, caught between a rock and a hard place, accept a lower standard of living. They simply refuse to participate. They go underground with their earnings, avoiding the Social Security tracing system. Some file bankruptcy when the Roman road to ruin becomes too odious. Populations migrate, as one historian put it, because of the unequal contest between people evading taxes on the one hand, and efforts of the bureau people to collect them on the other hand, causing citizens to flee civilization to live among the barbarians.

FLAVOR CREATES A BOTTOM LINE

Gearld Fry found a new bottom line within 30 miles of his Rosebud, Arkansas, home. He had been in business as the head of Fry's Reproductive Center, a venture that involved collection and processing of bull semen, embryo work, cow breeding, pregnancy checks, and the miscellany attending the profession. Fry was forced to turn the Center over to a son because of cumulative injuries to his knees.

Fry decided to finish out beef animals using nutritional principles documented in *Eco-Farm, An Acres U.S.A. Primer.* A federally inspected facility processed the meat and created a package suitable to the gift trade.

That trade, Fry reasoned, was a handshake away.

Fry simply presents himself to businesses, explaining that he, too, is a businessman, that he sells flavor in steaks and other cuts. He explains that he avoids the flat cardboard taste by never using fermentation products, hormones, antibiotics or animal fats in his field ration.

The product is out there in a refrigeration unit, held in his truck for instant delivery. Price is never a problem.

It took about five weeks to run out of the first 19 beef animals, and reorders and referrals have been coming in ever since.

Often buyers join Fry in a trip to the cargo trailer for instant delivery, cash on the line.

Eyeball contact is the key, Fry says. So is maintenance of control. The farmer who dumps his production into a sales barn or so-called market has no say-so as to price, and therefore abandons control over the bottom line.

Fry also serves as a reproductive consultant and scouts the county for superior beef sires.

It is axiomatic that businesses pay no taxes, that in the final analysis such costs become the personal property of the consumer. Thus we arrive at the first rule for bottom line preservation — all costs have to be passed on to the consumer. No tradition, government agency, or farm mythology can be allowed to stand in the way.

The veterinarian who comes to the farm charges a fee. To a migrant worker this fee seems obscene. He does not realize that the government's partnership in the earnings of the vet may take more revenue than the veterinarian gets to keep himself. Neither the migrant nor the farmer who gives him temporary employment realizes that the end-line consumer has to pay the taxes involved — twice! One payment is made when the service is rendered. The farmer must pass on the cost, and so the consumer ends up paying the cost as a higher price. He pays a second time when he pays his own taxes.

Farm organizations will object that farmers can't pass on their costs because institutional arrangements do not permit it. This is true, but only for the farmer who insists on taking at face value the garbage handed out by academic economists, flannel-mouthed politicians, and running-dog lackey types in command of the public prints and other media.

It is the purpose of this *Guide* not only to reverse those arrows illustrated above, but also to make an end run around the negative myths and fictions that have proved to be so debilitating in the past. The astute reader will have discerned many of the guiding principles by reading the first two general chapters. These principles will now be restated by the number, thereby supplying the rules for operation of a sound bottom line farm.

Archer Daniels Midland likes to run TV ads advising farmers, usually using a David Brinkley voice-over. One I recall told tillers of the soil about saving subsoil. Another explained how pasture could be turned into row crop acres for soybean production, ergo greater protein production to feed the world via the conduit of ADM, of course. But as Ann Clark of the University of Guelph in Ontario has pointed out, it isn't the farmer's job to produce more protein for the handlers, but to make enough income, enabling preservation of the bottom line. Few, if any, bottom lines can be preserved by accepting anything less than parity exchange in the marketplace. Self-reliance starts when a farmer thinks for himself, without a necessary reference to an approving authority.

CHAPTER 3

Rules for a Bottom Line

Land comes first. By hook or by crook, the use of land has to be arranged for, and its cost and depreciation figure in the flow of cash toward that legendary bottom line.

This chapter will codify and explain a cash flow statement for a 100-acre farm. These bottom-line results will not depend on any change in public policy or require anything rational to emerge from the United States Department of Agriculture. There will be no effort made to get big enough to contest the economic arrangements that now hold most farmers in thrall.

To those who object that agriculture can't be run this way, or that these ideas would collapse if too many people tried them, only one answer will suffice. Only a few farmers can be expected to get smart rather than bigger. Even fewer have the sand it takes to do some original thinking. Most growers can be expected slavishly to follow the advice of those dedicated to plunder. So back to our 100-acre farm. No guide could possibly answer all the questions the unique nature of land quality and location impose. The late Carey Reams used to punctuate his lectures with an exclamatory, "That's a rule!" Making a profit on the 100-acre eco-farm requires the discipline of rules that border, if they do not encroach, upon being absolutes.

Rule No. 1. Find the cheapest land available. So called worn-out land is best because the seller usually entertains a lower transfer price. In any case, it usually does not make good economic sense to buy fertility embodied in real estate of dubious quality. In truth, over the short and long run the 100-acres will have to be shaped and primed. Good road and bridge access to the 100 acres is an absolute necessity, and a reasonable distance to a fair-sized community is a must, as explained earlier. The transaction price for land has to obey the projection of the income statement explained below.

All Cost Per Acre Basis	1st year	2nd year
Taxes	$24.00	$24.00
Land	62.50	62.50
Tillage & Planting	35.00	35.00
Harvesting	25.00	25.00
Seed	20.00	0
Fertility	100.00	0
	180.00	60.00

Rotations Per Year		
2 year Corn 100 Bu.	$ 30.00 Bu.	$300.00
2 year Beans 35 Bu.	11.00 Bu.	385.00
2 year Split 3,000 #	200.00 P/Ton	300.00
Straw 100 Bales	100.00 P/Acre	

1st Avg. P/Acre 361.66 — 180.00 = $181.66 Avg. Profit
2nd Avg. P/Acre 361.66 — 60.00 = $301.66 Avg. Profit

Land Cost	$500.00 P/Acre
Interest	$125.00 = $625.00 ÷ $ 62.50
Est. Taxes	$ 24.00
	$ 86.50

1st year P/Acre $181.66 — 86.50 = Profit $95.16
2nd year P/Acre $301.66 — 86.50 = Profit $215.16

3rd & 4th year with average conditions, yield should increase 10 percent per year — with additional 10 percent totals for the 10-year period.

Wish book druthers, yearnings for bucolic scenery and neighbor-pleasing vistas are of minor importance when complying with Rule No. 1.

Rule No. 2. The soil has to be shaped in terms of fertility, always relying on the precepts stated in *Eco-Farm, An Acres U.S.A. Primer*, and in the materials recommended for additional reading.
The 100-acre grower has to evaluate every system in terms of three premises:
1. Is the concept to build new soil and start all over?
2. Will it add to the problem of excesses?

3. Or is the system geared to extracting from the excesses already there a little more energy, which would be akin to giving someone CPR who is already dead?

The 100-acre farm with profit on the bottom line cannot be a chemical farm, meaning that chemicals of organic synthesis have no place as an expense item, or as a management tool.

Leonard Ridzon of New Waterford, Ohio has the largest compilation of cash-flow statements for successful 100-acre farms that I have encountered. All start with the land and its reclamation. Ridzon's formula calls for up-front application of 500 pounds of Nutricarb per acre, plowed down, with a second 500 pounds dressed on top in time for spring planting, probably a legume. Likely as not there will be areas and acres that do not measure up. No problem. Cut the cover, plow the green stuff under, then plant spelt. Within two years that farm will be so profitable "you'll think you can buy the whole world," Ridzon says.

DOWN IN THE VALLEY

Hugh Lovel's farm, nestled in the gentle mountains near Blairsville, Georgia, provides a real-life example of biodynamic agriculture working in a commercial operation. Only 14 acres, his farm is a community-supported agriculture model.

The farm was literally a big gully not many years ago. With a steep hill on each side and a creek running through the middle, Lovel filled, leveled and built the beds through slow, back-breaking labor. Rocks from the beds became a roadbed; soil moved from the roadway became the garden beds. Through application of enlivened rock powders, biodynamic treatments, balanced micronutrient products, lime, compost, ash — the list goes on — Lovel has created rich, fertile topsoil where there was pale red clay. And it is the envy of the region.

There is almost no compsarison between his soil and the soil in the region. "It has a nice crumb structure; it doesn't just turn into powder when you crush it," he says. "A soil like this absorbs the rainfall instead of eroding.

Aside from superior crop production and quality, this fine soil also gives Lovel the advantage of a greatly extended growing season.

While neighbors usually plant in May and finish in September, he is planting by the end of February and finishes harvesting late in November, usually picking spinach and rape all winter long. "In fact, you'll actually get better peas, onions, spinach and lettuce by planting early," he says. And these are but a few of the more than 100 varieties he grows during the year for his 120-some customer families in Atlanta, a two-hour drive to the south.

Farsighted, Lovel established the farm as the Union Agricultural Institute with the hope that it will live on as a teaching farm after he moves on. He would also like to see urban agricultural projects as a way of helping our troubled inner cities.

In the meantime, the farm has an on-going bottom line based on correct technology and direct sales.

Whatever the crop — soybean, corn, spelt — it will be superior in protein content and worth a parity price, not on the junk grain markets, but in markets that serve feeders, dairymen and specialty trades.

Reclaiming soil is an art, one properly left to the purview of the several texts that deal with the subject without too much reference to the conventional wisdom of Extension, land grant colleges or USDA.

I have seen Austrian soils that looked like an Iowa gravel road turned into fine loam with the help of rye, biologicals, and timely incorporation of both into the soil, thereby giving the tired and worn out soil a fix of microorganisms and food for their survival. The spelt crop works equal magic, with one difference. In the case of rye as a green manure, the crop is utilized for fertilization. In the case of spelt, the high-protein grain is harvested for animal feed and human nutrition, and the residue is returned to the soil.

Rule No. 3. The 100-acre farm cannot compete with the mega-spread in producing bins and bushels of junk quality grain so deficient in protein it beckons decomposition in storage. Quality is hard to come by when commercial seeds, by law, require contamination to be inserted into the soil — Captan, for instance.

A normal wheat crop will bring in about $120 an acre, not enough to pay for car fare home, we used to say in college. A normal spelt crop will bring in $300 an acre. Because it represents quality, spelt is not a Board of Trade entry. Most of the traffic is conducted by private treaty, some of it in the export category. Quality does not permit toxicity, an impediment gifted even to organic production when aerosols pollute the environment. Many people attempting to grow organic are buying conventional seed.

Rule No. 4. Compute the value. It takes no mathematical genius to compute the values, both before and after they are produced. Arithmetic tells the farmer whether what he is doing is correct or not. Take wheat in central Ohio — 20 bushels to the acre. Pencil the harvest in at three dollars a bushel, or $60 an acre for such a modest harvest. Compare that to, say, spelt (actual harvest) 1,500 pounds to the acre at 10 cents a pound, or $150. Without departing from mainstay crops, the arithmetic indicates $150 as compared against $60. A few acres on that basis gives a hint as to what parity feels like.

The bad year illustrated above was selected on purpose. Normally an Ohio or Indiana crop will hit 50 bushels an acre, wholesale to the trade at three dollars. At the same time the spelt crop in the area, under the same conditions, weighs in at 3,250 pounds per acre, at a value of $322 an acre.

The average wheat grower spends $160 an acre for toxic technology. Subtracting that amount from his harvested $150 an acre return on the crop, the result is minus $10. Even a school child can do arithmetic better than that.

Most farmers, faced with such numbers, try to buy more land so that they can rectify this unreality by getting bigger and growing more volume.

Rule No. 5. Sell the crop at full parity. Parity simply means recovering inputs in the production process. Stated another way, it commands farmers to stop using inputs that cannot be recovered at market or make possible a reasonable profit. As Candy Johnson put it, "You have to add it to the price of the beans." A reasonable profit is six percent of the investment, and this cannot be achieved by dumping grain at harvest into international trade channels. All the chapters of this book have as their ultimate goal the achievement of parity — a satisfactory bottom line.

No one has written more on macroeconomic parity for farmers than I have over the past forty years. Yet I have to confess that the parity abstraction fails to consider the basic rule having to do with quality.

Most of the corn grown today in fact receives parity in the market. It is junk and receives a junk price. While agriculture in general carps about low prices, some few eco-growers spend more to transport corn than the crop is worth. Yet the feeders tell me they make more money with good corn at twice the price than they do with the mineral and protein deficient fare available nearer home.

A feeder who buys corn purchases protein and nutrients. Nowadays corn has five to six percent protein, not the 12 percent protein for which eco-principles account. In short, it takes twice as much of the lesser protein corn to even compare to the eco-corn. By using the best corn at twice the price, the feeder has half the freight to haul, half the feeding requirement, plus the other health factors conferred by protein at 10 to 12 percent, along with trace minerals. It takes quality to achieve parity, and parity to achieve quality.

Rule No. 6. Storage. Economically, the storage function belongs to the farmer. This was recognized by the Stabilization Act of 1942, which commanded parity for agriculture as part of the war effort. Indeed, USDA at one time touted bin construction for on-farm storage because it was understood that basic storable commodities achieve a 365-day supply and a one day demand at harvest. Once grain moves off the farm, control over its future is transferred to the middlemen. The 100-acre farmer therefore has to develop storage for at least 75 percent of the crop, and rely on quality inventory and control to govern release from storage.

Public policy is not likely to assist farmers. If such was ever the goal of the last half dozen administrations, it evaporated the day Ezra Taft Benson invoked the 60 to 90 provision of the Farm Act of 1949.

Since that day and hour cheap food has been public policy, it being understood that cheap food means hungry people in the fullness of time. This is exactly the way poverty programs create poverty. There is a perfectly wonderful market out there for high-value crops. The concept of bins and bushels is no longer suitable. Such crops have to be measured as protein and nutritional units.

Commercial storage merely blends good production with junk. The objective seems to be moving the mix before the decomposers of the biotic pyramid do their work. Quality determines whether crops will store.

Rule No. 7. Full Employment. The Full Employment Act of 1946 was written to protect the industrial labor force, largely at the expense of agriculture. Its position on the books made necessary the farm measures of 1948-1949. This piece of permanent legislation erased the mechanism needed to keep the aggregate of agriculture on a solvent course. Briefly, the 1942 wartime remedy required a loan mechanism for basic storable commodities. If the market failed to take the production at parity, the farmer had the option of putting his grain in the loan program. In theo-

AN ENVIRONMENTAL FARM

Richard and Sharon Thompson, Boone, Iowa, are outstanding in their field. In fact, Sharon often introduces her husband that way, with a slide of — you guessed it — Richard out standing in his field.

It all started in 1967 because the university/ USDA-touted system wasn't working any longer. Crops were faltering and livestock exhibited the effects. That's when this Iowa couple decided to go back to basics, then marched forward with innovations that complied with nature's rhyme and seasons. This meant rotations — corn, soybeans, corn — and growing rather than buying feeder cattle. The fences that had been removed under the Svengali-like spell of the get-bigger chant were replaced. Pigs were farrowed on-farm, and the Thompsons looked to using valued manures rather than buying commercial fertilizers. As a matter of fact, no factory-acidulated fertilizer entered the system for decades.

The goal, of course, was to farm without contaminating land, water or food. Compost suggested itself, and — in time — a potassium shortage made soil testing necessary.

There was a time when the Thompsons figured the crops and weeds would have to report the condition of the soil. This worked to such a degree, with soybeans, corn, oats and hay being produced on the farm, the Thompsons were pulled into the national limelight.

Selling clean beef and red meat was not enough. The world demanded scientific proof. The Thompsons held to their opinion that castrated beef didn't entirely measure up, thus no castration for young animals, and only a rubber band treatment later on.

Those 300 Thompson acres do not measure for much with those who think they have to farm several sections and end up losing the farm. But those 300 acres have provided for a family of four children, two of them farming. The economic numbers reveal that conventional-wisdom corn loses $30 an acre. Thompson's corn, in a five-year rotation, grosses $50 an acre and saves at least $45 on toxic supplements — a $90 differential.

The Henry A. Wallace Institute for Alternative Agriculture wants these facts to become common knowledge, for which reason the Institute has sponsored record keeping and testing that make the Thompson experience more enduring than ever.

ry, he could reclaim it when the market improved, or he could abandon the grain and thereby cancel the loan. In reality, the presence of a full-parity loan mechanism supported the market. The result was a prosperous agriculture and a series of balanced federal budgets once the war ended.

When President Clinton failed to sign the Farm Act of 1995, the most recent permanent law — that of 1949 — was invoked, technically. Attorney Jerry Barringer, then president of The National Organization for Raw Materials, and several American Agricultural Movement farmers filed suit to require USDA to install the necessary machinery needed to couple 60-90 percent parity. The court stonewalled the attempt and at exactly the moment in time when the judge took the case under advisement, a congressional committee reported out the 1996 Farm Act, henceforth the market, securely in the hands of grain companies, will command world prices for the American grower.

Several developments follow the public policy of 1946 through 1949. First, production technology became debased. Toxic technology received the imprimatur of academia and good husbandry bowed to factory-in-the-field procedures. Many farmers allowed themselves to be lured into a corn, beans and a Florida lifestyle as a prelude to bankruptcy.

Rule No. 8. The farm has to supply full employment. The 100-acre farm is more likely to meet this requirement because of the options it allows. Rule No. 8 thus gives way to Rule No. 9.

Rule No. 9. Teamwork. Success for the 100-acre farm is not likely unless teamwork achieves front burner family status. It has been said that Socrates might have been a farmer, much as earlier he was a solider. But with a nagging wife like Xanthippe, what else could he do except become a philosopher? Unless there is full cooperation from the wife and children, the 100-acre farm is condemned to failure. With cooperation, it can be the most successful institution for learning in the country and an excellent lifestyle business as well.

Rule No 10. Harvest in-kind values. A few years ago, at the height of the farm crisis, the public prints carried news reports of farmers standing in line with food stamps. These farmers had become factory-in-the-field people who produced for the international trades and didn't even maintain a garden or grow a potted tomato. Not many people understood such farmers, and I admit I have a problem with this type of agriculture. There are simply too many values on a farm to be had tax-free and to give them up in homage to the elusive nothing seems absurd.

Start with the premise that 52 cents of the national income dollar is sucked up as taxes — federal, state, and local. Each dollar taken off the farm as income in-kind is a more powerful dollar than the dollar returned from the sale of production. It may be that commercial foodstuffs are cheaper measured by the usual indexes, but home-grown and organic has more than quaint charm to recommend itself.

In a world polluted by gender-bender chemicals operative at one part per trillion, the only clean food you get may be your own. In the following chapters, I hope to illustrate the focus of all economic value. For now it is enough to get a measure on values that elude the great parasite concentration inside the Washington beltway.

Rule No. 11. Specialties. I have a Tennessee friend who simply can't get himself to do much other than grow hogs. This is a common trait among farmers. They want to grow what they want to grow, rather than grow what they can sell into a decent market. The Tennessean isn't hopeless, as I will illustrate in the next chapter. But maybe, just maybe, he ought to consider some expansion project to go along with his cherished occupation.

For the 100-acre grower, the big sky is the limit. I'm not even talking about the $3,000 per acre blueberry crop, or the trail into exotic orchids or herbs. The expansion role is available in the meat and potatoes business implied for the purposes of this chapter as corn, beans and spelt.

Location is critical, of course, because side money depends heavily on the nearness of people. The corn, beans and spelt producer can run a few hogs and chickens, as suggested in the opening chapters. Now we see how the several rules feed upon each other and merge, one furbishing and refurbishing the other.

Modern agriculture advisers sneer at the diversified farm. Peer pressure has been used to crowd the family farmer into getting too big until, like the serf in Russia at the time of Napoleon's march on Moscow, he can't call his soul his own. And yet 100 acres, with some applied intelligence, holds the key to $30,000 to $40,000 on the bottom line.

Rule No. 12. Promote the farm and its results. The 100-acre model farm may seem a perfect refuge for the introvert, but it is not. It takes a lot of names on the Rolodex or computer file to make up a customer list willing and able to pay for value received. Pork chops with essential fatty acids, beef production that allows the cow to remain an herbivore, chickens that eat grasses and salvage spilled grain, all need to be advertised, albeit not in expensive yellow pages or weekly papers. Most health food stores will either buy health food quality products, or allow bulletin board space for flyers advertising the farm and its products. Most 100-acre farms do not have time to entertain multiple projects. Still one or two mini-farm ideas plug in nicely under the right circumstances.

Rule No. 13. Be computer literate. Software for the farm computer is no longer the problem it was even a decade ago. This technology will generate all the paperwork even a despotic agency can require. Not many people can operate a farm and also do the accounting and legal work, time being the chief constraint. Therefore the association of an accounting firm, a small one, is indicated.

Rule No. 14. Budget time. The temptation for small- and medium-sized farmers is to do it all, and to take on a few projects beyond that. This became evident during the gasohol days, when thousands of farmers decided to make their own tractor fuel. In taking on this time-consuming work, they failed to remember the time requirement and some even overlooked the contamination dangers inherent in hasty work. Corn and beans do not confer full employment. Still other projects have to be installed to comply with time slots available.

Rule No. 15. Do your own thinking. Few occupations are as subject to peer pressure as farming. Folklore, much of it installed by mendacious people in the trades, the schools and the government, keeps the farmer off balance because he does not wish to be laughed at. This tribal habit has made it possible for the most outrageous ideas to surface as public policy, and the most absurd technologies to be touted as conventional.

Once farmers were asked to get bigger, get more efficient, or get out and they accepted this strategy, they were handed another morsel to digest. Their salvation, they were told, was to sell surpluses to foreign markets. Free international trade was the high road to unlimited prosperity and because they didn't think for themselves, they failed to realize that there have been no surpluses, except seasonal, since 1910-1914. Wheat and corn are said to be in surplus, but when factored into the aggregate of production, that national food pantry is short of self-sufficiency, hence, the open road for input invasion and price destabilization. Also, because they did not think for themselves, they paid scant attention to the fact that they were being taxed into oblivion in everything they purchased and deprived of the one thing they were entitled to: first crack at the American market. That market was handed off to traders who exploited foreigners. Domestic labor embodied in products has tariffs aplenty: Social Security, workmen's compensation, unemployment insurance, income taxes, property taxes, etc., whereas goods and commodities from foreign shores endured few tariffs, if any.

In failing to reject the flaws supporting big issues, farmers made themselves prey for advice designed to annihilate them as production units in order to gather the land into a few strong hands.

Economics is dominated by financial people — bankers, stock brokers, trust managers, traders, international shysters. All have an interest in taking wealth from producers and giving them very little in return. Whether the issue is national or logistic for the south 40, you have to think for yourself. The decisions are always in the grower's court.

Most critics of these few simple rules almost shake with anger as they attempt to poke holes in almost all of the 15 Rules. What about your N, P, and K, they fairly shout, girding for the attack. Yet the natural farmer who invokes *Eco-Farm, An Acres U.S.A. Primer*'s lessons, Podolinsky's knowledge, Albrecht's wisdom, and/or Ridzon's experience spend next to nothing for the salt fertilizers and rescue chemistry. The air is very near 78 percent nitrogen. The amount of phosphorus in the crop represents about a third of a percent — about eight pounds, 90 percent of which also is transported as particulate matter in the air, always serving stomata intake when enough carbon dioxide stimulates the plant. God knows there's plenty of fluoride in the air and any well managed decay system accounts for carbon in the air. These two, mixed, manage the magic of phosphorus for plant life. When muriatic acid is bonded with carbon, presto, a potassium supply is assured.

About two percent of the eight pounds mentioned above comes from the soil, a repository of enough material to last until the next ice age. A 10,000 pound crop of corn takes no more than a single pound of calcium, 33 pounds of potassium, and 25 pounds of phosphorus. A shell corn crop assembles approximately 80 pounds of nitrogen based on the protein level. The shell corn represents 25 percent of the total organic matter produced by that crop. This means that 75 percent of the nutrient load is returned back into the soil, where water and decay management hold their mother lode ready for the next growth cycle. Removal of one pound of calcium means three pounds are returned to the soil system. Removal of 33 pounds of potassium means return of 99 pounds.

The standard texts contain preposterous numbers that make bagged fertilizer traffic sound like high intelligence. But figures honestly treated do not lie. There is no net energy loss in the life cycle. Perverse management may result in nutrients being taken off the farm, and its loop-back to the countryside is devoutly to be wished, but these considerations do not mean a farmer should annihilate his bottom line with unneeded inputs on the one hand, and a final sale price that ignores operational parity on the other hand.

Generally speaking, the protein value in corn is 30 cents a percent. Thus 10 percent corn is worth three dollars a bushel. The same is true with soybeans. Soybean proteins constitute maintenance protein and are worth less than corn per percent, an energy protein. Leonard Ridzon and company compute his model on the basis of tested certified toxin-free grains calibrated in parts per trillion. This qualifies for profitable bottom line prices.

A rhetorical bottom line now presents itself. A farmer who wants a profitable bottom line and does not want to give up the toxic approach might as will hang it up.

CHAPTER 4

Opportunities Unlimited

The information furnished so far has been presented less to tantalize than to make a profound point. Just as the peasant has vanished from the scene, so has the production-only farmer. To survive and prevail, the farmer now has to become a farmer-entrepreneur. The days of seat-of-your-pants analysis has vanished, like the blunderbuss and battle-axe.

It may be that an inverted pyramid best describes the economy in which the farmer operates. Although raw materials provide the support system for the activities of mankind, it is nevertheless a fact that most of the multiplier rises from the plain exactly as mentioned above — as an inverted pyramid. This activity has conspired — if such a word is politically correct nowadays — to pay the raw product producer for less wealth than he has accounted for. The only way a farmer can hope to share an appropriate measure is to elevate the skills of agriculture to a multiplier level enterprise. In so doing the peasant-farmer is forever left behind, and the farmer-entrepreneur is born.

This has not been the perception of schoolmen and so-called public policy shapers over the decades of the 20th century. A few years back, John Kenneth Galbraith wrote *The New Industrial State,* an extrapolation of *The Organization Man* by William Holly Whyte. The perception of reality stated as an absolute in both of these landmark books was that super-organizations would provide employment, regulate commerce, create jobs and manufacture a higher lever of civilization in the fullness of time. This assessment has proved to be hopelessly and articulately wrong. By the last decade of the 20th century — with *Fortune 500* companies sending millions of jobs to low wage areas of the world — it had become self-evident that the industrial state was a fiction, and that the organization man was tied to the inefficiency level generally reserved for government workers or professionals best employed on killing fields. The 21st century seems destined to become known as the age of the entrepreneur, possibly the age of the farmer-entrepreneur. The unlimited opportunities for the farmer-entrepreneur have never been as great as they are today, and the prospects have never been so poor as they are for the man on the land who seeks to be no more than a production farmer.

The first to make the connection were perceptive consumers. They discerned a relationship between stale foods, spoiled foods, chemical residues and human health, and they slowly passed the message back to farmers. Only a few responded. Most growers failed to get the word. And without an idea inspired by the word, millions departed into the oblivion called bankruptcy. The Food and Drug Administration pretended that the nation's food supply was the best and most wholesome in the world, leaving it to researchers to identify the demonology that was visiting so much degenerative metabolic disease on the population.

The point could be made by examining grains, vegetables, fruits, whatever. For the purpose envisioned here, it will be enough to take a look at protein production.

Up front I am required to say that almost all of our protein meat agriculture damages human health and destabilizes human society. And yet I will stop far short of seconding Jeremy Rifkin's clarion call for elimination of the bovine species from planet Earth. The tragedy of our protein production has been recited in chapter one.

The point I am obliged to entertain here is styled base period 100, 1948. The year in which Congress passed a series of laws that lasted until 1996, and that in time destroyed the quality of the food supply on the premise that the untested technology being advanced made economic sense. Indeed, a new economic theory was pushed forward, one that stated as an absolute truth the proposition that food is much like any other product — and that farming governed by technology is the same as manufactures. This new truth held that as new technology is introduced, enhanced productivity and efficiency must follow as night follows the day. The pretended bottom line held that high science and technology would produce more food at cheaper prices, and therefore benefit the economy in the United States and people everywhere. Further, this system would be drawn capillary-style to the far corners of the world.

As with many obvious truths, the above proved to be hopelessly wrong, and its wrongness is kicking open the door to opportunities unlimited for the farmer-entrepreneur.

The precis on trade policies offered above must be multiplied a thousandfold when we attempt to factor out the task available to the entrepreneur of the new century. William Campbell Douglas, a physician, has identified no less than 1,200 grocery store products that contain the cancer causer aspartame.

THE BIG OPPORTUNITY

Most people think of Montana as the Big Sky country, a name conferred on the land by A.B. Guthrie in his great novel, *The Big Sky*. But to the late Ted Whitmer of Glendive, Montana, all of agriculture was "the big opportunity" of our era. That opportunity depends on intelligent cooperation with nature.

For Whitmer, the moment of truth came in 1959 when he realized he was going broke in spite of hard work and thrift. One night Ted came to the dinner his "sweetheart" had prepared and declared that the four bins of wheat he had would be sold at double the market price.

Whitmer had come to his senses. All his life he had produced superb crops using organic principles, but that quality was blended with junk and sold at half price. "No more," declared Whitmer, and by 1962 he waltzed into the bank and paid off a fistful of notes.

Whitmer continued producing organic spring wheat on his 400 acres, rasing a family mostly on home-grown food, secure in the knowledge that the greatest potential in the world was providing wholesome food so that human beings could mature, possessed of minds capable of thought and reason.

Neighboring farmers wanted him to sell their wheat to the niche market he'd discovered — "A little spray won't hurt," they said. Whitmer refused. A man without integrity might as well be stuffed in a coffin. Ironically, the nation was awash with food, but you couldn't find clean eggs, milk, poultry or red meat. With these observations in tow, Ted started Whitmer and Associates.

Whitmer must be considered a life-long role model farmer. His attention to sound principles of eco-agriculture predate Sir Albert Howard, and his influence is now being felt in numbers the movement only dreamed of a few years ago.

Whitmer was one of the great inspirations that kept *Acres U.S.A.* afloat and moving ahead.

Nutritionist Royal Lee, as well as W. R. Cox, the author of *Hello Test Animals*, brought to the attention of an unbelieving world how fluoride annihilated sex and health. The late Ted Whitmer, a Glendive, Montana rancher, computed the level of that enzyme destroyer in the gluten and bran of grain. It would take a book several times the size of this one to detail the abominations in the typical grocery store, restaurant and kitchen that cry to heaven for remedy. Only a favored few seem to realize that the allure of narcotics is spawned by stale and empty foods.

Since the Food and Drug Administration refuses to protect the food of the population, the task now falls to the entrepreneur, the very person Joseph Schumpeter said must ultimately destroy the existing order.

Those who have entered this arena have done so with dedication and aplomb. Some have failed, and some have given themselves a problem they did not have before: they now have to pay income taxes.

Having set the stage with pragmatic observations, some few case reports, and the reason for being of the new farmer-entrepreneur, we can now move forward to a step-by-step *how-to* program for success.

This is both a scientific and artistic approach. Certainly there is science and art in finding a need *and filling it*. Note the three words in italics.

Merely producing a crop or product is not filling a need. It is merely the opening gun of a war with sides that are not evenly matched and a playing field that is always uneven. Moreover, the plan — as with any battle — usually fails on contact. The winner in the entrepreneurial game is the farmer who gets there "firstest with the mostest" as General Bedford Forrest would say — the "mostest" being knowledge, ideas, focus, and resolve.

Over the years I have interviewed or visited perhaps a thousand farmer-entrepreneurs. All of them started with their idea.

Frank Ford started Arrowhead Mills while putting in a few thousand hours of tractor time in Texas high plains wheat fields. The thinking process went on for months, even years, before start-up, modification and success. By the time he retired and harvested the results of his efforts, Arrowhead Mills had become a household word. "I envisioned operating from the farm," Frank Ford once said. He went on. He savored the country scene and expected his lifestyle enterprise to disrupt his bucolic tastes in a minor way.

Ted Whitmer concluded one day that selling high-protein wheat at 50 percent of parity was a one-way ticket to oblivion. Without too much of a business plan, he started packaging his wheat and selling it catch-as-catch-can into the health food industry, such as it was. His board of directors

PRESERVING A FAMILY FARM

Innovation and adaptability are two words that describe Ken Soda's 40-year term of running the family farm several miles northwest of Princeton, in south central Wisconsin. He took over from his father in 1958, and has now handed the reins to his two sons, Steve and Kevin.

Ken's sons are the fifth generation to work the combination of low muck land and rolling sandy hills. Ken's great-grandfather established the farm in 1863, during the Civil War. The current farm of 870 acres (700 tillable) has been pieced together from three previous farms, plus Steve and Kevin rent another 300 acres.

Until 1962, the farm was a dairy with a few chickens. Ken had already been growing mint (spearmint and peppermint) for commercial flavoring, but decided to make some changes. He sold the cows and started raising chickens for the commercial egg market to provide continuous income while relying on mint and corn for cash crops. The mint is harvested as fresh green plants, then processed on the farm in a home-made distillery with concentrated, very odiferous, mint oil produced and tons of plant residues left over. One acre of mint produces about 50 pounds of oil.

That typifies Ken's approach to farming — using nature's systems to provide crop nutrients and build the soil and thus to keep purchased inputs very low. For the last ten years the operation has been recycling its own by-products of mint residues and chicken manure to form a high-grade compost, which goes on all acres each year. For the last six years they have also been adding 200,000 to 400,000 pounds of rough fish, or carp, that the state takes out of area lakes. And if the market price for old laying hens is low, the chickens also go into the compost windrows (both the fish and chickens are first ground into small pieces to increase composting action).

included Royal Lee, Jonathan Forman, William A. Albrecht and a few of the voices in the wilderness then decrying the lack of quality food on American shelves. Once he started thinking, Whitmer told me in the twilight of his career, the ideas shot into the open like a pent-up geyser. He started a consulting business, explaining Albrecht's science in the understandable terms used by people of vision, men like C.J. Fenzau, Neal Kinsey, Don Schriefer, Dan Skow, Walt Shuman, Elmo Robinson, Fred Wood and dozens of others then helping growers break with toxic technology and embrace the role of the farmer-entrepreneur.

There are some 10,000 protein meat producers who grow ostriches. They have their work cut out for them, not only in growing the birds, but in clearing a conduit into trade channels. I do not know whether success will attend all of these ventures. I do know that these are farmer-innovators who are ready to reject the idea that chickens, turkeys, cattle and swine have a hammerlock on protein meat production. Likely they would find intrigue in ecologist Edward Wilson. Ed Wilson suggests that certain species of turtles could outproduce traditional sources of protein if given a chance. Still, it is not enough to set up producers to set up more producers — worm ranch style — without attention to merchandising the final product.

Some few years ago I published a book titled *The Potential of Herbs as a Cash Crop*, by Richard Alan Miller. Miller had identified some 400 herbs imported into the United States that could be grown locally. He constructed production and business plans for clients and helped put to death the notion that a farmer could produce what he wanted and somehow the market would make things right with him and the world.

American growers produce hundreds of crops, not just the basic storable commodities the public prints talk about. In recent years the innovators have removed fish production from riparian avenues and installed the art into farm ponds. Vegetable, fruit and nut producers have mastered the production art without the use of toxic chemicals.

I do not want to suggest that organic is sweeping the field — far from it. Bill Lashnett, formally with NFO, has despaired of farmers ever developing the institutional arrangements needed to recover parity from markets dominated by world leveling factors. With a few associates he organized Farm For Profit, a group dedicated to finding the most efficient systems for row crop production. The first order of business was to cut pesticide use to the bone and better business arrangements for all the traffic connected with the farm.

Ideas spin off each other. One of Ted Whitmer's boys found his farmer-entrepreneur bent fulfilled in providing Montana legume producers with pollinator bees. Ken Soda, a Wisconsin mint producer, concluded that mint distillation and chicken production as well as compost making — plus other crops — annihilated the curse of the monoculture farm. Organ-

SUSTAINABLE STEPS TO PROFITS

Bob Quinn was raised on the 2,400-acre family operated diversified farm he works to this day. Located southeast of Big Sandy, Montana, the farm has been in the Quinn family for most of the 20th century. Holding a Ph.D. in plant biochemistry from the University of California-Davis, he started a small biological testing laboratory in Woodland, California in the mid-1970s, selling his business interests to run the family farm in 1978.

When Bob and his family returned to share the farm with his parents, the farm wasn't big enough to support two families. Half of their 2,400 acres was pasture and half of it was cultivated. Bob was looking for something to add value or increase income from the farm, and by accident stumbled into an opportunity to sell grain directly to whole-grain bakers. The bakers started asking for organic grain, Bob started Montana Flour and Grains and began buying and selling organic grain. By 1985, the Quinns added a flour mill and their organic niche continued to grow. They were soon supplying more and more organic product until, by 1988, they were 50 percent organic and 50 percent conventional. By 1992, they were 100 percent organic. Through the process the Quinn family became self-sustaining, eco-friendly, and profit-making. The education that really began during the process of starting the business, buying and selling organic grain, and meeting organic farmers gave Quinn an opportunity to see firsthand and talk to people who had success themselves.

Bob works closely with local Montana State University experiment station personnel testing different legumes and other crops as well as new farming systems which may be adapted to the northern plains and provide a substitute for the use of conventional fertilizers, herbicides, pesticides and summer fallow. He has been active in promoting organic and sustainable agriculture throughout the state and nation. He assisted in promoting the passage of Montana's organic labelling law and worked for the inclusion of an organic definition in the 1990 Farm Bill. Bob helped form Montana's first OCIA chapter and served as its first president, has served as chairman of the OCIA internal certification committe and secretary of OCIA International. He also was one of the 14 original members of the National Organic Standards Board. His commitment to organic agriculture is permanent.

ic performance not only enhanced quality production, but also became an "Open Sesame" to a better market dollar.

There are only a few thousand mainline farms in the United States, according to USDA. There are millions of units Gene Logsdon, the ag writer, calls "apparitions," meaning they have been removed from the statistical arrays and count for no more than the pushcart peddler under the manor wall of medieval times. But they do count and they can help destroy a system that no longer functions in a manner that can be calculated to help mankind. Each farm, large and small, is a capital pool for the farmer-entrepreneur. Each can spawn more ideas than a hatchery can spawn fish. To be meaningful, each idea has to be evaluated, then tested.

What is it about this or that idea that requires it to be taken seriously? How can it be subjected to rigorous examination?

Jack Graves of Troque Farm at Buckner, Missouri reasoned correctly, I believe, that one of the brightest opportunities in farming today is poultry production. Since the reasons for this were stated earlier, it will suffice to present a sort of Troque Farm balance sheet suggesting the reason for being of this idea (*see page 38*).

This is not the kind of balance sheet accountants construct. It is, however, the T-account that ideas demand. The product may be the buffalo meat Francis and Ruth Polifka produce at Catharine, Kansas, or it may be the flour mix Bob Quinn ends up with after harvesting high protein wheat at Sandy Point, Montana. It matters not, the pros and cons of the proposed enterprise have to be set down as if in brass before the farmer-entrepreneur can proceed.

Over the years, some farmers have complained that they didn't have the time to read and master the precepts of eco-agriculture. As a consequence, they have continued to accept orientation from Extension workers and university counselors that often as not has led to bankruptcy.

Mastery of organiculture as presented in *Eco-Farm, An Acres U.S.A. Primer* and works like *Hands-On Agronomy*, and *Mainline Farming for Century 21*, is assumed, as is acceptance of the proposition that the anatomy of weed and insect control is seated in fertility management. Those who think otherwise may as well close this book right now.

Not assumed is knowledge of basics in running a business, whether start-up or expansion. Once you have your ideas in tow, the chapters that follow will come to your rescue.

WHAT'S THE DIFFERENCE

TROQUE FARM'S CHICKEN	CONVENTIONAL CHICKEN
Unvaccinated	Vaccinated (immuno-depressant)
Full Beak (no cannibalism)	Debeaked (cannibalism a problem)
Probiotics (immuno-stimulant)	Antibiotics (immuno-depressant)
Composting litter in brooder (sanitized through decomposition)	Sterilized liter (sanitized through toxic fumigants and sprays)
Carbon/Nitrogen ration 30:1	Carbon/Nitrogen ratio 12:1
Practically no ammonia vapor/smell	Hyper-ammonia toxicity
Rest at night — lights off	Artificial lighting 24-hours a day
No medications	Routine medications
No synthetic vitamins	Routine synthetic vitamins
No hormones	Routine hormones
No appetite stimulants	Routine appetite stimulants (arsenic)
Natural trace minerals (kelp)	Manufactured and acidified trace minerals
Small groups (300 or fewer)	Large groups (10,000 or more)
Low stress (group divisions)	High Stress
Clean air	Air hazy with fecal particulate (damages respiratory tract and pulls vitamins out of body, overloading liver)
Fresh air and sunshine	Limited air and practically no sunshine
Plenty of exercise	Limited exercise
Fresh daily salad bar	No green material or bugs
Killed by slitting throat (per Biblical directives — see Leviticus)	Killed by electric shock (inhibits bleeding after throat is slit)
Carefully hand eviscerated	Mechanically eviscerated (prone to breaking intestines, spilling feces over carcass)

Processing uses 5 gallons water/bird

Guts cooked and rendered, then fed back to chickens

Effluent treated as sewage

Government inspected

Routine injections (anything from tenderizers to dyes)

High percentage liver rejects or (breast blisters)

Dead birds incinerated or buried (possible water contamination)

Sick birds destroyed

Manure fed to cattle or spread inappropriately (ammonia vaporizes — air pollution, nitrate leaching, water pollution)

Toxic germicides to sanitize processing facility

Cooking loss 20 percent of carcass weight

Short keepers (freeze only 6 months or less)

Drug resistant diseases (R-factor Salmonella)

High saturated fat

Up to 40 chlorine baths (to kill contaminates)

FDA-approved irradiation (label not required)

Environmentally irresponsible (hidden costs)

Promotes feudal/serf agriculture

Centralized food system (promotes low wage/time-clock employment)

Urban expansion

Consumer producer alienation

Poor, flat taste

Inedible

Processing uses 2.5 gallons water/bird

Guts and feathers composted and used for fertilizer

Effluent used for irrigation

Customer inspected

No injections during processing

Low percentage rejected livers or carcasses

Dead birds composted

Sick birds put in hospital pen for second chance; most get well

Manure falls on growing forage and active soil for efficient nutrient cycling — converted to plants

Fresh air and sunshine sanitizes

Cooking loss 9 percent of carcass weight

Long keepers (freeze more than one year)

No drug-resistant diseases

Low saturated fat

No chlorine baths

No irradiation

Environmentally responsible

Promotes family farming

Decentralized food system

Rural revitalization

Consumer/producer relationship

Rich delicious taste

Edible

A DESTINATION FARM

Jack Graves' Troque Farm is a destination farm for clients from the Kansas City, Missouri, area. Troque is a French word, the pronunciation of which has generally evolved into truck, as in truck farm. In Louis XIV's France, troque farmers were specialists who learned how to grow certain crops out of season for royal tables, always guarding their secrets the way commercial companies patent theirs today.

"That's where the similarity ends," Jack Graves is quick to say. Graves is one of the new brand of farmers now populating the edges of cities and/or within 30 driving minutes. Many of the troque farmers come with a plan, and from the moment they arrive, they plan their work and work their plan. They know business procedures, have commercial experiences too diverse to list, and computerized income statements, balance sheets and cash flow statements to a fine point before they turn a tap.

Jack studied eco-farming before beginning Troque Farm. "We simply realized the need for quality foods for ourselves," he says. "This need wasn't confined to the family. The data I put together said this need was flowering everywhere." Biodynamic growing was especially appealing, and so he purchased a piece of ground — 125 acres — in the rolling hills east of Kansas City. Only 40 acres were tillable, but that's all Jack Graves and his family needed. The wilderness land remains wilderness, except for the ginseng Jack hopes to grow under the canopies of trees in mycorrhizae-rich soil. A few cattle can run on the rest, "rest" meaning land which is not easily tilled or subject to the modification eco-farming requires.

Jack Graves can confirm a tremendous market for range-fed chickens. People come willing and able to pay premium prices for fresh birds. Chicken sales are counted in the thousands, each sale a profit item; processing proceeds every three weeks, usually on Saturdays. The first batch of chickens were sold before they were grown, and that has remained the *modus operandi* ever since. In fact, Graves confirms, people are lined up for chickens months in advance, the market is that good.

Lamb, beef, and turkeys round out the production sequence, except for vegetables, and greenhouse production that promises year-round employment. Beef and lamb are processed off-farm; small animal protein production, rabbits for instance, are processed using some of the same stainless steel facilities that keep the chicken production line moving.

Customers stream to this destination farm on signal each week, almost all in response to a few small ads and word-of-mouth publicity. Consumers all realize that it is a privilege to buy clean, hormone-free meat and chickens not polluted with arsenicals, antibodies, coccidiostats and other strange alchemies. Steer meat protein is sold in advance, all of it at a healthy profit.

Troque Farm forms alliances with other farmers who use similar methods. Such an alliance gives the farmers purchasing power and holds out the prospect of a permanent location for the pooling of produce. This enables farmers to provide customers with a greater quantity of produce and meats.

Troque Farm expects to space cashflow so that there is revenue each week of the year. Cashflow means full employment.

Adding value to the raw product is the key to profit making. A farm kitchen, approved and certified, is a value-added operation. Packaging adds value. Growing chickens in 10-by-12-foot moveable pens adds value because of the green diet. Custom grinding feed adds value to the product of the field. Wholesome feeds subtract the costs of medications from the minus side of the income statement.

Jack Graves credits Joel Salatin, author of *Pastured Poultry Profits*, as the innovator and teacher in this emerging poultry game.

CHAPTER 5

The Key to Prosperity

It has been computed that the United States has to create 10,000 new jobs every working day in order to keep pace with population growth. That computes to 2.5 million jobs per annum. During the last half decade of the 20th Century, even half-fast thinkers in government and its clone corporations came to realize that small business entrepreneurs had to generate most of the new jobs. The appropriate conclusion is at once apparent. Millions of new jobs had to be created, or else the entire American structure was destined to slide into convulsion.

The record is clear enough. Some 21 million jobs were created in recent decades. These jobs were not created by *Fortune 500* firms or the relief client corporations that support war material creation for the world's killing fields. No, indeed, some 77 percent of those jobs were created by only five percent of the young and growing entrepreneurs, many of them start-up businesses.

Farmers, self-employed individuals, and small entrepreneurial firms accounted for the lion's share of employment in the United States during every recent decade, "lion's share" being taken to mean almost all of it.

Many of the start-up companies of the 1990s were lifestyle firms. The entrepreneurs involved chose to stay where they were and harness their resources to the new realities of commerce: instant communication, rapid transport, markets in motion from sea to sea, and even into foreign countries.

More important than employment data is the fact that new enterprises create most of the innovations. In a world that has so perverted science as to threaten its own annihilation, the farmer-entrepreneur — with a tap into nature's pure knowledge — has the crowbar it takes to pry open the values a health-conscious public needs and wants.

The cutting edge of perception of value to the farmer-entrepreneur was fashioned by health care providers. A few were establishment medicos. Most were simple people who could reason and face down peer pressure. Their existence within hours after the arrival of a sanctified chemical age required involvement of farmers. The distant goal even then was the proliferation of therapeutic food. The most astute saw an eventual transfer of expenses from sickness care to health care based on therapeutic food, a concept establishment medicine pretends not to understand.

The ideas that flow from the farm and reconstitute themselves as farmer-entrepreneur objectives are virtually unlimited in scope. To suggest that lifestyle enterprises, organic farms and customers on the hunt for clean, wholesome foods will one day destroy the existing order may seem preposterous.

More likely, the farmer-entrepreneur will simply enter the existing market. He will do this because he finds a need and fills it. Others will join the fray in the fullness of time. We like to believe that not many people will eat modern broiler house fare once wholesome, low-fat chickens become available, but that speculation skirts the certainty that consumers do not beat a path to the doorstep of the better mousetrap creator. They have to be sold and serviced, and that objective requires an organization and a plan.

In fact, the plan has to be a package of plans. Growing blueberries, raising Thanksgiving turkeys, or harvesting wormless corn on the cob is only a toe in the door of farmer-entrepreneurship. The art and science of soil management and crop production can be taught to anyone willing to reason and listen. Much the same is true of business entrepreneurship. The process is simple in the extreme. Psychologists tell us that there are no measurements that can be styled psychologically sound, at least not in terms of units with equal intervals and with an absolute zero. Thus, the entry of art. As Field Marshal Rommel said, "You can wage battles, but war is an art." You can audit the style and progress of a business, but enterprise is also an art.

The business process best starts with innovation — the idea, if you please. For many the process stops there. For psychological reasons that are difficult to appraise, the necessary triggering event never arrives. A decision has to be made, and those who have difficulty deciding simply have to allow others to accept that challenge. Once action has been triggered, implementation has to follow, the objective being growth and the bottom line.

Knowledge of the field has to background any venture. At issue, always, is risk — the risk inherent in dealing with people, associates, employees, and the public. Education, either formal or on the job, is mandatory. Personal values figure.

The world is full of unrecognized geniuses, people who can grow the prize orchid or farrow the best hogs. That much accomplished, they simply cannot face the stress elements inherent in business enterprise. On the other hand, the security of the big firm is becoming more of a myth than that of the Daniel Boone self-sufficient subsistence farmer. Talent is often submerged by comfort and complacency. While I was handling an editorial pencil for *NFO Reporter*, it was not uncommon for quiet farm boys to be volunteered to their feet, barely able to say a word. Coaxed into discourse, they gave their names and then started talking about their farm operations. In weeks they became spellbinders and organizers. After the grand movement went into decline, many became farmer-entrepreneurs, sometimes growing and selling specialty crops, often entering the fed cattle business, otherwise extending sweat equity into entrepreneurial co-objectives.

WORK THE PLAN

Dreams can come true with a lot of hard work. Peter and Billie Chimino, Reynolds, Georgia, were living in Tampa, Florida, where Peter worked as a dentist, but they wanted to live in the country on some land. All of Peter's life he dreamed of living on the land and farming, but as a city dweller he figured he "didn't stand much of a chance." As time went on he and Billie throught more and more of leaving the city. Their dream came true a few years ago when they bought a 550-acre farm, originally built in the 1840s, with an old pecan grove and lots of fields with room for the 14 dogs Billie has collected since she moved to the farm.

They are learning organic farming from the ground up. "We work harder than we've ever worked before," says Peter. They follow sustainable methods, trying to increase soil fertility and tilth, hoping to attract beneficials. They try to keep a cover crop going year-round and leave clover pathways around their market vegetable garden. Weeds are handled with a mechanical cultivator very early, then with lots of hand work. Although they have only been farming for a few years, their crops have done well so far.

This year, the Chiminos are renting part of their land to a neighbor farmer, and with him are growing organic soybeans on another part of the land. Peter hopes that by doing a joint organic project, he can convince his conventional neighbor to consider sustainable or organic methods. As Peter says, "We want to spread the word."

They produce squash, corn, watermelon, cantaloupe, several varieties of beans, and cucumbers. Tomatoes, peppers, eggplants and organic pecans are sold through an organic co-op in the region. In addition, they sell some goods at a friend's roadside stand. They want to sell as much of their product locally as they can, eventually building an on-farm trade.

The Chiminos are also renovating an on-farm log cabin, hoping to supplement the farm income by renting it out to hunters who want to field train their dogs, to people who would like to come for a weekend and participate in the you-pick vegetable garden, or just to anyone who would like to see a working organic farm.

Here the task remains: plan the work and work the plan.

SUPERIOR GRAINS

Marvin and Carol Manges, Yale, Illinois, farm 700 acres in the east-central part of the state. The farm was originally Carol's home place and they began farming it in 1977. Carol says she became interested in ecology while still in college and enjoyed discussions about Rachel Carson's *Silent Spring*. Even so, when they began farming they went conventional, but became very unhappy with chemical farming in the mid-1980s. They now have 400 acres certified organic by OCIA. The remainder of the acres, some newly purchased, are also headed for organic certificaiton.

By every measure of results, they are highly pleased with their program. The previous high costs for fertilizer and chemicals are gone, soil health is greatly improved and they enjoy growing markets. They have organic markets for white food grade corn, for red, yellow and specialty popcorn, wheat, yellow corn, and Clear Hilum soybeans. The white corn goes to tortilla chips and the soybeans go to Eden Foods for soymilk.

They have good yields with their orgainc methods of crop rotation, ridge-tilling and rotary hoeing. Under their system, something green must be growing at all times. Still, there is no hard and fast rotation. Corn yields range from 100-125 bushels per acre. Soybeans generally yield 44-55 bushels per acre. "We take a lower yield than conventional farmers, but our markets more than compensate for that. In any case, our soybean yields are high average for the area, and our market advantage more than compensates us," says Marvin.

Marvin and Carol agree that the soil is God's greatest gift and "we are the caretakers, not owners of this gift. If we take care of the soil, it will take care of us. Our stewardship involves a total system approach. With crop diversity and rotations, and cover crops which recycle plant nutrients, we are seeing soil life return to our once compacted and lifeless soil."

Conversion is never an accident. It answers a plan made as a plan anticipates a bottom line.

Jim McHale, a farmer and farmer's union organizer and Pennsylvania Secretary of Agriculture, left office with a great deal of informal education in tow. He was one of the first national leaders to embrace eco-agriculture. His first love was production — as is the case with most farmers — and he saw a new requirement for soil system management after the basics were in place. The firm of J&J Agri-Products came into being. McHale continued to operate the farm with his wife Jane (J&J), but now he joined dozens of other enterprises springing up to help the new agriculture chip away at the pseudo-scientific approach cemented into place ever since the universities discovered that chemical companies had grant money.

The farmer-entrepreneur has to be a leader, or grow in that direction. He has to dream dreams and see visions (Joel 2:28), and he has to be connected to the work at hand. Most of all, he has to have accumulated knowledge only hands-on experience can account for. The apartment dweller with *Mother Earth News* on the coffee table needs a little more than a dream to make a farmer-entrepreneur blueprint work.

Stating these things in abstract form may not communicate the message as clearly as I would like. Therefore, please let me recite a few personal notes to illustrate how background and life experiences can influence the outcome of the venture.

I have always enjoyed working with words — the word wrangler, the cowboys called me while I was writing copy for *Rodeo Sports News*. I grew up on a Kansas wheat farm, and worked at a miscellany of jobs that filled two single-spaced typewritten pages when I was being checked for security clearance during World War II and the Korean War. I reported football for the *Chanute Tribune* (Kansas), installed copy into the lockup chase for the base *Rev-Meter* in a reconnaissance technical outfit during the Korean affair, and finally packaged two college degrees into a job running nine trade papers. Still, agriculture remained a first love, a proposition I demonstrated, I hope, as a publisher's assistant for *Veterinary Medicine* magazine, and again as editor of *NFO Reporter* during the prime Oren Lee Staley years.

By the time the idea of *Acres U.S.A.* came to consume my thinking, I had more than a seat-of-the-pants idea of where I was going and how I would get there. The methodical approach used and the lessons learned fit hand-in-glove with those needed to start-up a farmer-entrepreneur launch off the time-honored plain of production and "what'll you give me" sales.

I could, if I wished, list all sorts of impediments and blame government policies for the difficulties imposed on the farmer-entrepreneur. This would be less than counterproductive. Nor do I intend to downgrade chance encounters as the genius of a venture.

Bill Holt, the astute proprietor of Fermented Products at Mason City, Iowa, used to explain why he was in Mason City — "a place colder than Siberia" — when his first love was the South. "Why are any of us where we are? That's where I got off the train and got my first job." Mobility has increased since then, of course, but the fact is that many people find careers in the first job, regardless of education. Many farmers are now poised to extend their first job on the farm into the multiplier sector of the economy.

Some of the most successful entrepreneurs come to their crowning achievement simply because they run out of career options, are victims of corporate downsizing, or because they pause long enough between farm chores to realize that they are going broke and need to do something different.

Business schools and university researchers compute that 95 percent of all new ventures are introduced in fields already occupied. Almost all entrepreneurs simply hatch their ideas out of work experiences.

It was experience that enabled me to sort out the procedures and parade across the examining board the instruments of analysis that had to pave the road.

I have already discussed the farmer-entrepreneur idea and proposed a T account for study of its ramifications. Suffice it to say that few farmers know enough about the crops and services they might want to produce. Research and rapport with Extension for technical bulletins are in order. If the target project involves, say, soybeans for the tofu trade or export to world areas that favor such a food crop, it becomes incumbent on the farmer-entrepreneur to know all there is to know about the crop or product. Ditto for shiitake mushrooms for the restaurant trade, or any other idea product that promises a decent bottom line.

This exercise usually is not a problem for the farmer-entrepreneur. Know all the rules for a fresh and wholesome food supply. But those untried uplands of business and marketing — necessary adjuncts to production agriculture — require new exploratory thinking.

My own approach, an approach gifted to subscribers and clients over the years, is set down here in outline form with a promise that each proposal will be extended in depth and related to real situations so that the reader can draw the appropriate conclusions.

After the farmer-entrepreneur idea has been examined, fleshed out and fit into the mosaic of the whole, the first element of integrated papers must be constructed.

The first paper in the sheaf of documents most bankers and many support organizations will require is the business plan.

Agriculture today no longer permits the question: are you the entrepreneur type? The answer has to be yes if you wish to survive or prevail. The suggestion that a farmer should remain some sort of rural shift worker simply has to be dismissed, and all those articles with numbered questions might as well be quick flash material for the home fireplace or the shop's pot-belly stove. If you can't stand facing people, try a Dale Carnegie course before attempting to write a business plan.

That much said, know that it is not enough to bow to coffeehouse peer pressure that holds to the walking IBM machine theory. That sort of cowboy arithmetic may have served in a simpler era. Today it walks hand in hand with the conceit that a verbal communication can be filed and retrieved in a court of law.

The earlier illustration that set down as a T account the difference between an Arkansas broiler and a free-range chicken illustrates the diligence required to cover all the bases.

Gene Davis of International Resources Unlimited in Eugene, Oregon once delivered seven plan-related suggestions to a Washington State University assembly of farmers. According to Davis, a consultant, planner and engineer, the business plan must show "a clearly stated goal" to be achieved fearlessly and without vacillation, cite information gathered from all pertinent sources, and all this information should be coordinated to reveal how the goal can be reached. Included in this package should be available information assembled from similar types of endeavors, including production, engineering, financial, marketing, human resources, etc. Risks that might interdict goal achievement should be spelled out and juxtaposed opposite remedial suggestions. Not least, financial projections covering cash flow, profit and loss and balance sheet data are indicated. The assumptions and the rationales supporting them must be presented clearly in simple English *sans* double-meanings or hedged phrases. Alternative financial sources to bridge cash flow shortfalls must be a part of the plan, and rate attention in importance with the basic entrepreneurial idea itself.

No less than seven components of business success must be digested and made part of the plan:

1. The idea comes first. "In the beginning was the word."

2. Resources come next. They must be inventoried and literally cast into bronze as the intellectual exercise called "the plan" takes form, gathers speed and moves ahead.

3. Processes involved must be clearly understood, not only mechanically, but also in terms of legal requirements, availability of services, and capitalization.

4. Products, of course, link the farming craft to entrepreneurship.

5. Markets are the targets for product flow.

6. Markets, sometimes structured, sometimes yet to be developed, demand as much analysis as several of the other components combined.

7. Management is merely an extension of a skill the farmer turned entrepreneur has exercised in developing his brand of biologically-correct agriculture. Additions to this outline must recognize two considerations so closely related they constitute the same side of the same coin — finance and environment.

Davis holds that usually prospective entrepreneurs, especially farmer-entrepreneurs, lack an understanding of one or more of these major business success components. Any shortfall in comprehending even one of them can undermine the success of any venture.

Friends, business connections, contacts — all are of maximum importance in bolting together that first clear statement on where the enterprise hopes to go and how to get there. Without the above — which the farmer is obliged to consider — opening or expanding a businesscan be a lonely exercise.

The grab-bag of information available to the farmer-entrepreneur isn't the only consideration. It is the sunshine lamp that fellow businessmen can provide that often helps the new enterprise get off the floor.

The folklore that beats eardrums into a bloody mess has it that only one business in ten survives to reach a tenth birthday. This is errant nonsense. Many of the two million businesses that start each year live on, whereas exhausted entrepreneurs often simply close up and never ever touch bankruptcy court. A lot of businesses fade away like an old soldier. Many are lifestyle affairs. Actually the odds are closer to one in four, and the survival rate of those that do their homework seldom clogs the bankruptcy statistics. The chances for a second generation owner are equally attractive.

Withal, it is enough to point out that a new farmer-entrepreneur arrangement is almost always a love affair. As with marriage, anyone can enter. It takes judgment and maturity to survive and prevail. So let's flesh out the plan. For a moment it may seem that we're kicking over the inkwell on blotter paper to see which way the capillary action will take the dark liquid. But that is not the case. Before we're finished, you'll know whether your idea means prosperity unlimited or whether you'll have to go back to the drawing board.

CHAPTER 6

Crafting the Plan

It is not very likely that the companies that style themselves venture capital firms would have any interest in the farmer-entrepreneur proposed here. Nevertheless we can profit from the criteria they use to evaluate an idea. Without exception, they look to three components when offering capital resources to a venture. These are:

1. Opportunity
2. The entrepreneur
3. The management

Most of them want other than borrowed money — "even the guy's wrist watch," one venture manager told me — because the person with nothing invested will falter when patience is required, and slough off when round-the-clock work is mandated.

A well-drafted plan will identify problems before they cut the legs out from under the farmer-entrepreneur. Many a first-rate plan goes down the tube because it is made to depend on second-rate management. Further, a great management team is of little value without resources.

Up there in the rarified air where money people decide on what they back, they have a saying: "Never back a second-rate man with a first-rate idea. Better to back a first-rate man with a second-rate idea."

Questions and answers that attend any farmer's venture into the business of getting paid for as much wealth as he produces generate a lot of paperwork. As the idea reaches maturity, it becomes necessary to assemble the parts into a written plan — a blueprint, if you will. This seems superfluous to amateurs who exhibit the impatience that often leads to failure. Professionals know differently. It has to be done "to sharpen your wits," one consultant told me, "and to refine the upcoming scenario."

A first draft is that; a first draft. If typed, set it up quadruple spaced for easy insertion of notes. Keep margins wide in the extreme for notes that stream of consciousness accounts for. Above all, the narrative draft must answer questions about the proposed development, marketing, production, and — not least — selling approaches. Most consultants will not take seriously any venture proposal that has not explored in depth the critical issues of "Where are the customers?" "Have any of them been contacted?" or, "Are the idea and its projections so much ink based solely on fond hopes?" All this has to be put into a selling document, or the opening gun in the business plan.

Other than steeling yourself against the proposition that you might be wrong, the real readers of the plan should be kept in mind. These are the friends who will critique the blueprint, any and all who you hope will help grubstake the business, i.e., people who can issue counsel of value, financial advisers and resource providers, albeit not necessarily customers. A mixture is essential because not all who critique a plan have the same purview. Some may have more than an academic interest in what happens once the plan has been critiqued.

When circulating a plan, guard unique ideas. If banker counsel is sought, see if a picture of Benedict Arnold decorates the wall.

Institutional lenders shy away from fad projections and get-rich-quick proposals. Both seem to depart as quickly as they come. And yet angel financiers often exhibit greed beyond the dreams of avarice, always with caution, of course.

High rollers often prepare several plans, each targeted to a different clientele. This is mentioned as an aside because farmer-entrepreneurs have a hard time writing one plan, not to suggest even more. Multiple plans have to use the same sets of data, restricting the presentation to rhetorical changes.

Bank lenders are interested in cash flow, not pie in the sky. They exhibit extreme jaundice in the examining eye when the business blueprint promises returns well outside the industry norm.

No plan should run more than twenty pages, even if the language is crisp and to the point all the way. This rule is somewhat flexible, depending on the height of interest expected from the reader.

Some consultants will not allow anyone to read a plan without signing a non-disclosure document, but this precaution probably is not indicated for most farmer-entrepreneur start-up ventures. The reason is that the most valued critics may not want to participate under an atmosphere of "distrust" and intimidation. Distrust is set out in quotations because non-disclosure implies reckless disregard for the work of a friend and a lack of diligence in seeking advice.

It is always difficult for professional writers to understand why so many people agonize over the task of stating a few business truths simply. Yet those same writers would face an internal combustion engine with abject disbelief and helplessness. Admittedly, the writing chore is difficult for many. Often the paragraphs of a plan emerge too abstractly or they lack organization. Editing a work is often as difficult as writing it in the first place. The cautions issued to first-year college students can be applied:

1. Have a rationale buttressed by documented support for claims. This statement invites the use of examples replete with support of footnote quality to shore up statements and projections. Government figures, published studies, case reports, all add up to sound support. If a blueprint statement holds that a perfectly sustainable market exists for range-fed chickens or non-Alar apples, then have something to hang your

STARTING SMALL

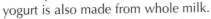

Who would have thought that one milk cow on 150 acres in 1976 would have turned into a yogurt processing plant supplying two major distributors? Such is the development of Butterworks Farm in Westfield, Vermont. The farm is guided by the skill and labor of Jack and Ann Lazor, their daughter, and others. Beginning with processing on the kitchen stove and delivering to 20-plus families, the Lazors decided to enlarge their operation in 1984. They built a barn, obtained used equipment, and acquired the needed licensing for raw milk, yogurt, and cheese processing.

Their crop rotation includes plowing down alfalfa or grass in order to grow corn, then soybeans, followed by two years of cereal grain with mammoth red clover underseeded the first year. Their demand for organic milk has increased to the extent of needing to grow organic grains for cows on another farm. By applying dolomite and rock phosphate, the Lazors replace the calcium and phosphorus that leaves the farm as milk. They keep the carbon and nitrogen on the farm as part of the nutrient cycle.

With Jersey cows producing four percent butterfat, this is bottled and sold as cream. The business of processing includes 80 percent of the milk used for non-fat yogurt: plain, vanilla, and lemon. Plain and maple yogurt is also made from whole milk.

Many farm families need off-farm income in order to remain on the farm. At Butterworks Farm, Jack and Ann consider the dairy processing and marketing as supporting the farm and supplying the extra needed income. Processing happens three days weekly with extra workers in the dairy and as drivers. They still have their own delivery route, plus two major distributors pick up at the farm. With local workers hired, the wages stay in the community, similar to what small rural industry was like in Vermont before World War II.

Needless to say, a plan cannot look down the road by decades, except in abstract form. Here the original plan was modest, yet it involved growth.

hat on with confidence. Personal knowledge in the form of case reports can be used, albeit not in excess.

2. Do not try to write the plan as a committee. One person, usually the best available writer, should be given the notes, special paragraph drafts and, not least, access to all contributors, to background the final polished draft. The old joke about a camel being the issue of a committee has its point. Even if several people become involved in writing several plan components, it is best to have one scribe do the final writing, otherwise the document is almost certain to end up as chloroform in print.

3. Set a deadline and stick to it. Business success is governed by an ability to meet deadlines that would make a newsman cringe. The time to impose this discipline is now, while the start-up analysis is in process. Procrastination undermines progress. Nothing annihilates profits and success half as much as failure to give top priority status to the blueprint plan in process.

4. A literate outside reader-editor should be asked to give the final documents a "do circulate" imprimatur. Only an outsider editor can be relied on to subdue the narrative, eliminate trade jargon and figures of speech of minimal value in communicating to the outside. Generally speaking, avoid lawyers and cost accountants.

Foreigners who write booklets in English have to use a polisher, one who grew up with English and won't be led into foreign language dictionary mistakes, especially errors in grammar. The bridge from a trade discipline to an outsider is often a trail without rails. Does the banker know what a gilt is? Only if he's used to dealing with farmers. So far, the nomenclature of organics and soil science is equally a mystery to those not familiar with the grammar of the subject.

5. Rewrite and polish. Don't let a sacred phrase cloud the issue. Very few people can write good prose via dictation, even with years of practice. The only accomplished master history has to offer is Winston Churchill, who rarely took pen in hand, and never, never used any of the tools we consider standard — the typewriter, dictaphone, computer. He spoke his rhetoric to a secretary who took down every word much like a court reporter. Few who have not been writing copy for decades are able to furnish suitable prose with a first draft. Therefore, rewrite and then rewrite. But never allow the process to become destructive.

6. The plan is never finished. It needs to be updated at least once a year, as do the flow sheets, cash statements, balance sheets, etc.

Having stated these several points, it becomes necessary to state anew the due diligence requirement.

Many prospective farmer-entrepreneurs object that they do not have time for what appears to be an academic exercise. Thus they arrive at the simple point that supports the entrepreneur and his business plan. We all have the same amount of time — 24 hours a day. How we use that time is the point in question. Competent use of time is the one requirement

A SHENANDOAH VALLEY FARM

Polyface is a family farm established by William and Lucille Salatin. Located southwest of Staunton, Virginia, in the scenic Shenandoah Valley, the farm is currently operated by Lucille Salatin, her son Joel, his wife Teresa and their children Daniel and Rachel. William's father, Frederick Salatin, was a charter subscriber to *Organic Gardening & Farming* magazine, and was a master gardener and craftsman from Indiana.

When William and Lucille Salatin moved to the Virginia farm in 1961, they brought the

Salatin tradition of organic farming with them. Joel and his family are the third generation to continue the principles based on the belief that God cre-ated the earth and humanity as its steward, to nurture, protect and embellish. This philosophy precludes the use of toxic chemicals, debasing substances, and erosive practices, and instills instead an insatiable thirst for agricultural truth.

The truth manifests itself in natural principles of plant and animal life. The farm should capitalize on these laws rather than fight againt them.

Roughly 550 acres, the Polyface Farm is about 100 acres of open land and the balance is wooded. The farm produces organic, grass-fattened beef, home-grown broilers, firewood, eggs, rabbits and vegetables. The Salatins are full-time farmers who are not independently wealthy; they rely on the farm for their sustenance, and have developed production, processing and marketing systems that make an end-run around agriculture's roadblocks.

The Salatins are enthusiastic and optimistic about farming. Joel has written a book, *Pastured Poultry Profits*, describing how his family manages their farm and how anyone willing to work hard can farm successfully and healthfully.

no innovator or businessman can dismiss. Time, in fact, limits ideas too grandiose to be accomplished.

Take this example. Carl Garrich of Paragould, Arkansas ran the usual diversified farm. In Arkansas this meant a rice production component. Ideas about further diversification floated in over the transom like autumn dust. But reality said that the family and available help couldn't do much more. This meant revenue-yielding crops geared to delivering monthly cash flow were not in the cards. A perfectly unique market for rice presented itself. Erehwon in Massachusetts wanted organic rice. The very idea drew gales of laughter from so-called conventional veterans. In fact *Farm Journal* published an article explaining how Garrich had decided to cut production in half by using Fletcher Sims' compost hauled in from faraway Deaf Smith County in Texas. The crop shortfall didn't materialize, but the sales did. They expanded to serve the therapeutic needs of victims of synthetics, pesticide contamination and unwholesome fare.

FACING THE SELLING WALL

Kip Mortenson is an organic farmer who clearly has the practical side of eco-agriculure down pat, but openly admits the fact that he's still searching for the Rosetta Stone of marketing success.

He and wife, Odette, raise organic beef in this traditional beef/sheep country of West Virginia. Mortenson, although working with sheep in the past, for about eight years concentrated on alfalfa and small grass production. After entering the vegetable business with about five acres of gardens, he discovered he was slowly exporting the nutrient levels of the farm. After buying the adjacent farm in 1989, he was back into animals with the raising of Hereford cattle — now accounting for about 80 percent of the operation.

The farm is certified organic by the Mountain States Organic Growers and Buyers Association (MSOGBA). Although never heavily chemically farmed, the Mortenson's are finding the land responding well to the techniques of sustainable agriculture.

The backbone of his program is on-farm composting. He produces about 400-500 cubic yards of compost a year and has his own turner. Poultry litter is both readily available locally and is cheap.

"I'm seeing fertility improve," Mortenson says. "Health and insect problems, while not gone, are waning dramatically — especially in animal health." A few years ago he began experiencing perfect calving periods with no losses.

On-farm, spring-fed drip irrigation systems are sometimes used in this fundamentally grassland area.

The Mortensons are retailing 30-pound boxes of assorted cuts directly to consumers. They've toyed with various types of marketing, learning on their own, and have met with mixed success.

"We tried dehydrating vegetables to make soup mixes for hikers, but the labor cost was too high," Mortenson says. They have also supplied a local CSA with meat, as demand outstripped that group's supply.

"I'm optimistic," he says, "but I keep running into a wall on the marketing side. Until society decides to support agriculture, it's an uphill battle."

"Probably the most rewarding thing that has changed for us is our recent involvement with a local non-profit group," he says. "We are starting an apprentice program through West Virginia Extension."

Health Education Action League (HEAL), founded by Theron Randolph, M.D., is a group whose members all have problems living on groceries which have artificially prolonged shelf life (read shelf death). These are the customers who factor into new farm enterprises because they are ready and willing to buy — if you can find them.

The point here is that these markets are not fad markets, and they do not invite a rush to enter. They do require construction of a careful entry plan to be administered by an entrepreneur with plenty of on-the-job experience in allied pursuits.

Minimum capitalization often will suffice. Mike Lundquist of Buckner, Missouri capitalized his farm by buying it on time, exactly the way one buys a city home. His job schedule with the telephone company enabled him to install vegetable plots, and Consumer Sustainable Agriculture (CSA) locals helped him build a market. One of these days the energetic young man and his family expect to cut the umbilical to the industrial paycheck because the farm is moving ever closer to sustainability in an economic sense. Other revenue producing ideas are standing in the wings — picnic facilities, perhaps a bird slaughtering operation, etc.

Such young enterprises are viewed exactly the way the baron once viewed the pushcart peddler selling his wares under the manor wall.

Progress has to be planned, and it has to be refined exactly as suggested above. Even with maximum capitalization, the market has to be identified. Bart Ehman of Petaluma, California, in fact identified a market dissatisfied with poultry that tasted like cardboard and yielded an unwholesome odor when remanded to the stewing pot. Chinatown restaurants wanted poultry grown in the traditional way — free roaming and fed humanely to produce wholesome meat. The birds had to be delivered with heads and feet attached, properly eviscerated and cold, not frozen.

Bart sold out, having made a great deal — "a satisfactory amount" — of money, and Petaluma Poultry is now serving that trade exactly in the manner originally planned. Even the government inspectors bowed to the wishes of this ethnic niche in allowing feet and heads to remain attached as demanded by that culture.

The writing of a plan implies the availability of an information material overload merely hinted at so far. In the next chapter, I'll plug in a sweep of details and make a few suggestions, it being understood that the final assembly of facts and ideas is up to the entrepreneur of each individual farm.

CHAPTER 7

The Prospect

Using our typical 100 acre farm as a metaphor, we can now bring into play raw numbers for the purpose of analysis. There probably isn't much purpose in belaboring costs once we eliminate pesticides and all but the most judicious use of so-called commercial fertilizers "which become available outside the biological system," as Alex Podolinsky put it. These considerations will surface soon enough, albeit not while we're considering the first profit and loss entry in our trip to the bottom line.

We have to accept the fact that there is no such thing as a typical farm. The styles of farms vary too much to permit an all inclusive, comprehensive income statement here. However, on page 58 is a sample framework, no more, it being assumed that individual famers can insert their own accounts.

If you pencil in the numbers, real or projected, one thing comes clear, high fixed costs are the norm, as are low variable or out-of-pocket expenses. Adoption of the ideas in this *Guide* cannot recast American agriculture. The rift between public policy and reality is too wide. But it can give a heady assist to the 10,000 to 20,000 farmers who read and act on lessons contained in this book.

The signal word is gross and how to kick it high enough so that the costs in production, fixed and variable, can be subtracted, leaving a bottom line.

We have seen that 10 percent protein corn at three dollars a bushel, assuming average production, factors out at approximately $400 to $500 an acre.

Take soybeans, 60 bushels to the acre at $10 average, 42 percent protein. Extend the arithmetic and you have $600 per acre.

FARM INCOME STATEMENT

INCOME:

Sales of Livestock		
Commercial livestock sales	0.00	
Sales to individuals, beef-sides, etc.	0.00	
Crop Sales	0.00	
Custom Machine Work	0.00	
Commissioned Beef	0.00	
Other Income	0.00	
Total Income		0.00

COST OF SALES & EXPENSES:

Truck Expenses	0.00	
Conservation Expenses	0.00	
Custom Machine Work	0.00	
Depreciation Expense	0.00	
Feed Purchased	0.00	
Fertilizers, etc.	0.00	
Freight Out & Trucking	0.00	
Gasoline, Fuel & Oil	0.00	
Insurance	0.00	
Interest — Mortgage	0.00	
Interest — Other	0.00	
Labor Expense	0.00	
Rent — Vehicles & Machinery	0.00	
Rent — Land	0.00	
Repairs & Maintenance	0.00	
Seeds & Plants Purchased	0.00	
Storage & Warehousing	0.00	
Supplies	0.00	
Taxes — Land	0.00	
Taxes — Other	0.00	
Utilities	0.00	
Veterinary, Breeding & Medicines	0.00	
Other Expenses	0.00	
....	0.00	
....	0.00	
Total Expenses		0.00
New Income or Loss		0.00

Wheat — well, we can't deal with wheat. The international character of wheat, and imports — paper arithmetical — keep the so-called staff of life at world prices.

In place of wheat, the 100-acre farm has to go to dinkle or spelt, the invested gross remaining the $400 plus per acre discussed earlier with 100 pounds of straw and 3,000 pounds of grain. Straw is generally worth one dollar a bail, sometimes two dollars.

One hundred acres at, say, $500 per acre come to $50,000 gross, all common crops.

Specialties can deliver another $17,000 to $20,000. These are not exotic specialties — just sweet corn, tomatoes, potatoes.

The only way the 100-acre farmer can expand his gross is to add to the production effort.

A small cattle producer should be able to grow out 25 cows. Sale price $900 a head, cost $350 to grow. Twenty-five at $550 equals another $10,000.

An add-on of 50 hogs, average $200 each, pumps up the gross another $10,000.

So far the equation has deflected away from becoming too labor intensive.

Numbers, of course, are numbers. By allowing hard reality to intervene, we have to adjust numbers to the vagaries of the weather and the market. To be fair, you probably can't get much above $60,000 operating as a mainline diversified farm. That's meat and potatoes farming.

Once exotic specialties enter the picture, the dimensions of the gross change. There are growers in semitropical areas who gross $150,000 per 10-acre farm. But those who perform this miracle literally live in the field. They spend no time at the coffee shop out-bragging their neighbors. Moreover, they usually have available plenty of good help, usually immigrants who have not become afraid of work.

There are enough case reports to prove any point. For instance, I know of a family with 25 acres in Illinois. These acres used to produce chiefly Mexican tomatoes for chili and ethnic dishes. Few people seem able to grow this crop, but these folks do the job on carbonized soil. There are a lot of grandkids involved for labor. Such an operation needs more land about the way one needs a hole in the head. The family could not work much more. Still, everyone is being paid. The bottom line in this case was $21,000.

These data may not be brilliant, but they are real. Most farmers are not able to do as well.

This may seem odd, but odder still is the fact that most entrepreneurial-farmers are better off than 90 percent of those who attempt a business venture. Up front, they are decision makers. They are planners. They are managers. Bringing bounty from the earth and managing animals and the assets of a farm requires as much. The only shortfall seems to be exposure to the outside world and its business requirements.

It is said that Sam Walton reduced the usual management overload from ten to four, a number most farm operators have bested, taking size and scope of operation into consideration.

These points stated, we can now proceed to identifying broad concepts to be considered in evaluating a plan, in this case a farm near 100 acres.

Case Reporting

A man I will call Eli Pieter is a duck farmer. That of course is not his real name. The details supplied here are too personal to permit actual identification. Eli grew up with duck production from when his grandfather raised those webfooted friends and in time he came to know ducks the way some men know the sea. Between childhood and middle age the world turned over several times. Specification buying and vertical integration swept agriculture, touted by Harvard economists.

Eli decided to obey his intellectual advisers and get big, which in this case meant installing facilities capable of growing out 40,000 ducks as a batch. A processor took the birds in hand at the end of each run, returning practically nothing to Eli for labor and no profit. In addition to duck production, Eli maintained a 35-milking-cow herd on his 160 acres (divided almost equally in ownership between Eli and his father). A $50,000 mortgage clouded the operation including two duck facilities. At one time the ducks were allowed to range freely, but this practice was stopped when government agencies complained that the birds defecated and that runoff water sometimes carried liquid fecal matter into a nearby stream.

In addition to ducks and dairy animals, Eli grows spring and winter wheat, oats, several vegetables and spelt. Most of the grains are used to feed his avian crew and dairy animals. Vegetables are slated for the Chinese ethnic market.

Last winter one of the bird house roofs collapsed and not all of the damage was covered by insurance. This disaster was compounded when duck grower Eli found himself without a contract because he had asked for a deal that would pay him at least a minimum wage.

This may have been a blessing in disguise. The farm has always provided full employment — too much employment, in fact, since Eli was always trying new things and stretching himself, his wife and son to the breaking point. In the end, production went into markets on a "What'll you give me?" basis.

Local farmers once tried to organize duck production. The effort went down in flames. Certified organic a few years ago, Eli dropped out because of the public's confusion over the names and functions of so many certifying agencies. Moreover, the paperwork involved seemed to require fruitless effort.

After conversation with a diversity of businessmen, including this scribe, Eli decided to develop a farmer-entrepreneur plan. He read the advice on drawing up a plan, and concluded correctly enough, that style and rhetoric did not insert substance into the effort. It was not a case of solving a problem, but one of bringing dozens of problems into a coordinated package. No one can give numbered expression to such a process, but the goal is worth a try.

A slight impediment to finding a solution is seated in the fact that most farmers love production and avoid in-depth business dealings, especially selling. The refusal to deal with certification work was perhaps a correct decision for the wrong reason.

SERVING CHEFS & GOURMETS

Greg Sava's Brier's Run Farm spreads over 160 acres in the center of West Virginia. The Savas bought it in 1975 after leaving upstate New York. They lived in a tent until they could build a room. The land was farmed out, with the rocky soil covered with thick briers. They cleared and plowed the land, one holding the horse, one holding the plow, surviving on native ingenuity and neighborly help. Greg says, "The neighbors gave us plants every time we came by." Mrs. Sava adds, "West Virginia has incredible warmth. They did not want us to go hungry; there was an incredible sharing."

Over the years, the couple tried a series of enterprises to eke a living from the land. Eggs, strawberries, corn, doll-making, selling fencing — none afforded them a decent return on their labor. Then they bought their first goat from a preacher. "She cried all night. She kept us awake. They want company because they are a herd animal," explains Mrs. Sava. They bought the rest of the preacher's goats.

The goats produced more milk than the Savas could drink, so they decided to make cheese. They experiemented and made many mistakes before deciding in 1985 to make chevre. More and more gourmets were accepting it as a tastier, healthier alternative to cream cheese. It was almost an immediate success. Even before they developed their recipe, the Savas sent a questionnaire to the ten best restaurants in the state, as picked by a local newspaper. Have you heard of chevre? Would you use it? Would you buy it from a local supplier?

Brier's Run was the first cheese plant of any kind to be licensed by the state of West Virginia. It is also the first goat cheese producer in America to be certified by the Organic Crop Improvement Association, whose seal of approval is known around the world. Now chefs all over the East Coast are using Brier's Run's chevre, which comes plain, herbed, fresh or aged.

In addition, the Savas market fromage blanc, a fluffy light fresh cheese; quark, a thick yogurty concoction; and fudge that Mrs. Sava makes by hand every Friday night. One chef at the National Press Club in Washington, D.C., commented: "They make the cheese when I order it, which is a nice thing. They're not pulling stuff out of a warehouse for us. This stuff is handmade. It's like ordering a Rolls-Royce that was made by hand for you."

Success has not translated into big bucks for the Savas, but they don't measure success by the dollar. "We've done it all ourselves. That counts for something. This house won't make House Beautiful, but it doesn't leak, it's warm and it's ours. You know, it's unique."

One additional possibility developed as the above points were being considered. Son Joe — after mature evaluation — rejected the idea of becoming a salesman. His skills were seated in repair work, especially tractors, farm and household equipment. With land, a building, and parking space available as a site for consideration, such a shop could be opened in connection with a sales facility at the farm. Of all the possibilities, it appears easiest to build a *pro forma* gross receipts and/or income statement for this new farmer-entrepreneur venture. The going rate for repair work away from a dealership is $24 to $26 an hour. An eight-hour day times five days in a normal week yields 40 hours, or a gross of $960 — close to $1,000 a week. A small markup on parts can be reckoned to expand the gross even more. Extra hours mean extra money, and success in, say, lawn mower repair and/or snow blowers could easily allow the business to grow into handling chain saws; both for sale and repair. Of all the mini-income (or subsidy) statements required to strike the overall totals, this one would be the easiest to construct together with a check number annotation. A simple alphabetical file should be sufficient for most small start-up enterprises.

Accountants need no further explanation, and those who do not have accounting training would be well advised to hire an accountant.

After nearly a half-century of effort, some few consumers look to clean, wholesome food to subtract costs from the medical equations imposed by AMA (American Medical Association) in dealing with degenerative metabolic diseases — cancer, Alzheimer, Lou Gherig's Disease, Parkinson's syndrome, etc.

These several considerations hold organic food to a higher level of performance and impact on the business plan Eli hopes to construct. The several items that follow have to be considered individually and as they relate to the entire package.

Item 1. The term organic may not be available to separate junk from quality in the near distant future. As with most words in the English language, it has several meanings, one of them being opposite the generally held concept. Thus, chemicals of organic synthesis are said to be organic when in fact they are manmade molecules. Several dozen agencies and organizations certify products to be organic, and the federal government has its Organic Standards Act, administered by USDA, presumably in response to suggestions from an appointed board. The board proposes, but the government is not obligated to listen. The situation suggests a potential for ultimate destruction of the organic idea as efforts made to call genetic engineering "organic," or to make way for exceptions, readily suggest. Whether to develop a trade name or to rely on the public's perception of organic as clean, wholesome, fresh, etc., is a matter for studied consideration.

Item 2. The prospects for dairy production are not bright, even under trade name or organic standards. Eli has noted that the system defies a consumer to get a glass of fresh whole milk. Bovine somatropin and trade practices have made the product suspect. For instance, milk is adulterated with materials that qualify as "fat," but these are inserted after butterfat has been removed for industrial uses, and the milk itself has been homogenized and pasteurized, making it troublesome in human digestion and implicating "the perfect food" in heart problems that have become pandemic. Although there have been no milk-borne diseases of scope in 50 years, the milk codes get thicker year by year, forcing dairy farmers to cope with an awesome and expensive inventory of regulations.

Item 3. A debt of approximately $50,000 hangs over Eli's farm, a consequence of expansion and construction of buildings that now stand empty. This debt is not great, but it encumbers all acres. Should Eli find himself in a liquidity crisis and unable to service this debt, the entire farm would be in jeopardy.

Item 4. Eli is concerned about endangering the farm. A student of cycles, he is aware of celestial alignments that took place on April 20, 1990, wherein Jupiter and Saturn influenced sunspots and the flow of energy to planet Earth. This phenomenon occurs every 179 years, and is always attended by hard times within the decade that follows, lasting from fifteen to twenty years. Although not a trembler, Eli is cautiously optimistic and therefore reluctant to take on more debt, or even to carry the debt he has.

Item 5. Eli is an artist at his craft. He has never suffered an epizootic or loss of flock and always produces a healthy product without resorting to vaccinations and hormones and arcenicals. He knows the breeds, hatchery sources and some potential customers for delivery of either live, cold or frozen birds, and has experience with UPS and Federal Express delivery.

Item 6. An overburden of work has kept Eli from selling his product, even though he has proved himself a "good" salesman, his Dutch accent not being an impediment.

Item 7. Eli's son Joe, is in his early thirties and employed off the farm because of liquidity problems. He may be willing and able to hit the road running, and shows promise if introduced to the trade enough to get the feel of things.

Item 8. Like most farmers, Eli is concerned about pricing himself out of the market. In dealing with wholesalers and middlemen, this decision is taken off his hands. In fact, he produces the birds and in effect asks, "What'll you give me?" Or the arrangement states simply what will be paid, and the prices never have a relationship to costs of production.

Item 9. Eli has dabbled in vegetable production, bok-choy, cabbage, and lettuce, the idea being that production from a few acres disappears into a local co-op. The jury is still out on this part of the farm enterprise.

Item 10. Eli has discovered a system for growing ducks with low fat. They require a few weeks extra feeding of sprouted grains to replace greens available to the birds before bureaucracy discovered the ducks shamelessly defecating in the field. His system permits manure recovery and salvage of the fertility value with insertion of an additive into the slurry and direct field application.

These ten items are merely so many precis of consolidated breakdown of the operation as is.

Eli is a highly intelligent farmer, a good manager, a decision maker. He understands national economics as few congressmen do, and he is quite aware of the ploys used to keep farmers in absolute penury.

A longtime reader of *Acres U.S.A.*, Eli has had little difficulty identifying with the mental attitudes a change of venue proposes. In order to construct an income statement, or to flesh out the one he has on the farm going into this new start-up venture, certain breaks with the past appear to be indicated.

Debt and cows seem to be holdover problems more than loss of production contracts. The cows take too much time since they require milking morning and night and other chores related to their maintenance. The debt has become something of a carbuncle to Eli because he has a great deal of knowledge about convulsions on the curve of history. Since the dairy cows can be sold for a price that in effect washes out most of the debt, this suggests itself as a recommendation.

WALNUT ACRES

Paul Keene, Penn's Creek, Pennsylvania, was an early role-model farmer for *Acres U.S.A.* He went into sustainable agriculture in the 1940s when farmers across the country were turning to toxic technology in record numbers. A burning cross in one of his fields and threats of dynamiting his barn were the responses Paul Keene received when he went back to the land. Why this strange welcome? Paul was "different" — he was a former college professor who farmed naturally. He plowed with horses when local farmers were turning to tractors. And he believed in being an active member of his community.

After serving as head of the mathematics department at Drew University, Paul went to India to teach in a mission school and learn how to live a more contributory way of life. While there he met Ghandi and Nehru, and became familiar with the farming methods of the father of modern natural agriculture, Sir Albert Howard. He also learned about Sir Robert McCarrison's studies on the effects of natural nutrition on the human body. Paul was convinced that natural farming was the way to produce healthy food for the world.

When Paul and his wife Betty returned to the states, they worked to buy their own farm. They put all the money they had into a 100-acre farm in Pennyslvania. Then came the burning cross. The Keenes stayed on, eventually creating the mail-order market, Walnut Acres. Their first product was Betty's apple butter made from unsprayed apples. Walnut Acres grew into a million-dollar business and Paul and Betty provided jobs to the Penn's Creek community, eventually offering employees profit sharing and mutual ownership of the company.

This much accomplished, the form of organization for the farm should be scrutinized. At age 58, it does not seem wise to operate as an individual proprietorship much longer. In the event of death, the farm's partner, Internal Revenue Service, would arrive and between death taxes, lawyers, appraisers, judges and shysters of every stripe, the heirs would find themselves skinned and lucky to walk away with car fare home.

Eli has options, but the one I like best is the trust. The trust creates an artificial person that does not die. As envisioned for this case, it would have its own IRS tax number, with administration in the hands of the designated administrator, Eli himself, and several co-trustees, namely his son and family members.

This isn't tricky and it doesn't pretend loyalty that isn't there. Most important, it avoids franchise filings and keeps the affairs of the farm private.

Eli should avail himself of advisers who could constitute a board. These should serve without compensation, or be paid as progress indicates.

The first figures on the income statement define gross income. Eli's ducks have been shipped from coast to coast, albeit always through the conduit of commercial processors. By stepping away from this treadmill, Eli can harvest many of the profits of the middleman, but he has to reclaim middleman functions. Moreover, he can claim premiums and gourmet prices by expanding on the reputation he already has.

This last suggestion is not pie in the sky. Paul Keene, a fellow Pennsylvania producer, asked and got $70 for a Christmas turkey during his prime years. A tray of chickens with the Walnut Acres label looked like the national debt to people who glory in the cardboard meat out of Alabama, "but they pay it!" The old idea that the organic producer should sell for 60 or 70 percent of what chains charge at retail is errant nonsense. If the product has value, then it should command a value price, not from chain store customers, but from enlightened folks who know the difference between health and sickness.

Most ducks are grown out in six to seven weeks. Growers nowadays are so-called independents. "He" — the middleman — "sets the price on the ducks, he sets the price on the feed, and he sets the price on the ducks going to market, and he isn't required to take them either."

Eli has rapport with the fellow who raises the best ducks on Long Island. He hatches them — an altogether different enterprise. The bird of choice for the organic-gourmet Chinese/Asian trade is the Peking. There is also a good market on the Muskovic, a slow-growing duck without the excess fat short-term breeds are noted for. It takes fourteen weeks to grow them. A hybrid French Muskovic takes twelve weeks to achieve maturity.

Commercial feeds — starter or forward — all loaded with fat from animal protein factor (APF). Eli often wonders how many times that fat has been recycled as one generation is fed to the next generation.

There's the art of complying with nature's requirements, and this means home-grown grains and sprouts.

The new start-up has no more problems than most enterprises, once the matter of target gross has been settled. The new gross relies on taking on middleman functions such as slaughter, sales, shipping.

Ducks are processed differently from chickens. They are bled and scalded, of course, but there is plenty of technology for small to mid-scale processing. Three styles of slaughter are accepted by the trade, ethnic and otherwise.

After feathers are removed via agitator, birds are dipped in hot wax and they pass to a cold bath. This permits the wax to be stripped off, removing down. Not a problem, other than employees, withholdings, taxes, workmen's compensation, insurance, etc.

Sometimes the birds are eviscerated, and packed according to market.

1. The regular duck market. Here the ducks are eviscerated, chilled, vacuum packed, then frozen. Feet and heads are removed. Some birds are sold fresh and cold.

2. A second market calls for blood and feathers to be removed, the pack that brought on the famous Schecter Poultry case under Roosevelt's NRA. Guts stay in. These birds depart into the market fresh, hurriedly it is hoped.

3. The ethnic trade wants the bird eviscerated but the head and feet attached.

There are a few live killers — a market Eli intends to enter. One contract for 2,500 ducks a week eluded him for want of financing. Live sales as a prelude to on-farm processing impacts on second and third generation dry run income statements.

Lesser factors also beg computation. Ducks are grown on plastic coated wire. Manure — which is 95 percent water — is harvested every day, held in a lagoon, then remanded to the fields as fertilizer. Some of this valued resource is given away. So far no attempt has been made to inoculate or compost the material because it would require a great deal of carbonaceous material.

With a full complement of ducks entering the system every two weeks, the run comes to a quarter of a million ducks a year — and an inventory of manure sufficient to tax the ingenuity of say, a Malcolm Beck.

There are always more ideas than time to bring them to fruition. Sweat capital has brought Eli's farm to its present start-up farmer-entrepreneur base. The next step will be to construct a *pro forma* set of management statements, income statement, a balance sheet, a cash flow statement, and a checklist of "must do" items that have to attend the entrepreneurial process of any successful venture.

CHAPTER 8

A *Pro Forma* Profit and Loss

Most of the elements required for a *pro forma* profit and loss (or income) statement construction have been cited or at least suggested. Indeed, heavy emphasis on needs assessment, markets, management, and business procedures, all have been treated in a brainstorming way. Actual finance will be deferred to a later chapter because the *pro forma* will suggest the route.

Appropriate Avenue

Before the *pro forma* profit and loss is constructed, all the points made so far in the narrative should be formalized into a check list. The list should have major topics and check items under each body. The list will vary according to the farm enterprise involved, including geographical location, proximity to population centers, trade practices, etc. The "etc." can be listed as follows:

1. Check accuracy of all information uncovered in the development of the first draft plan.

2. Review litigation, rules and regulations concerning production, handling, movement through trade channels and liabilities associated with the proposed plan. Many things can happen. Only one or two ever will. Therefore it is not necessary to conjure up hazards that might be only as real as being struck by a falling meteorite.

3. Reexamine business history, intractability of trade practices and the acceptability of innovation.

4. Customer habits, especially those of ethnic markets, must be viewed with empathy.

5. Compute preliminary resource requirements.

6. Cost out processing equipment.

A DRYLAND FARM

Leonard Mosher, Cheyenne, Wyoming, is third-generation farmer who works 1,500 acres of land straddling the Nebraska-Wyoming border. He has been organic for a long time, his father having taught him the practice. This part of the country receives only 13 inches of rainfall a year, so it literally takes two years of moisture to raise one crop. Accordingly, half the land in this strip-farming operation is always idle.

Growing the Scout 66 variety of hard red winter wheat, chosen because it survives the occasional hail well, Mosher tires to do everything himself — growing, harvesting, and marketing. "We have stricter harvesting practices," he says. "We like it drier and harvest slower — we get a much cleaner wheat."

His organic practices are quite the opposite of his neighbors who apply nitrates. He has found, however, that if they do anything, these synthetics shrivel the kernels and fail to raise the protein content.

"If we don't have moisture, the chemical wheat shrivels up," Mosher says. "If we have extra rain, they leach down into the soil and don't do any good. And when the neighbors use anhydrous ammonia, the weeds come in and take all of the fertilizer."

Working light soils overall, parts of his fields are slightly to the clay side, other areas sandy. He's used a moldboard plow for years — and has found good results with deep plowing, with an occasional presence of Canadian thistle being his biggest problem.

He markets his wheat both through the local elevator and direct to consumers, offering wheatgrass and home flour mills.

He has not certified his crop as organic because when he started there was no organization to check. "If you grow organically here, you are kind of on your own," he says.

The elements of a profit and loss statement take on a different complexion from many others for an operation such as this. The nature of the operation determines tax documents that describe it. Developing a specialty market now becomes the objective.

7. Codify processing knowledge.

8. Codify husbandry practices consistent with the goals of the enterprise.

9. Spreadsheet market analysis.

10. Extend number nine above into marketing plan.

11. Evaluate risk factors.

12. Evaluate the availability of employees suitable for the work at hand.

Skills required to build a *pro forma* income statement are seated in the farmer-entrepreneur, to be sure, but the refinement the task demands calls on the discipline of an accountant. Nor can the income statement stand alone. A balance sheet covering assets and a cash flow projection are equally important. None can stand alone if they are to be of maximum value, and all have to be integrated so that a change in assumptions on the statement can call for appropriate assumptions on all the other statements.

Filling in the figures for this *Guide* would be illusionary since inflation has a hammerlock on the nation, making such data too temporary, and ratio numbers better in tune with the times.

When I first laid out projections associated with the start-up of *Acres U.S.A.*, I considered an income statement still in use. The raw outline of that statement is depicted on page 70. Such a statement, with variations for type of enterprise, is valid for almost any farm enterprise.

The one item that was perfectly on target as an opener was the percentage and dollar figure amount covering income and printing costs. The printing costs especially could be targeted with accuracy because controlled circulation was to be replaced by paid circulation on a continuing basis, keeping the press run stable. The percentage figures lined up as illustrated within a year and have not departed that norm since.

Any accountant is familiar with generally accepted accounting principles. Coordination between the skilled farmer-entrepreneur and the figure engineer is bound to point up aspects of the proposed enterprise neither of them know pragmatically.

This caution is issued not to back off an entrepreneur, but to help him or her find lethal snares and make meaningful extrapolations that a linking of the several statements can account for. Computer nerds often dazzle the observer with spread sheets that walk forwards and backwards at the same time, but without an understanding of the overall projects, such machinations are worthless.

Plainly stated, not many accountants or entrepreneurs can assemble a valid set of projections in the time frame generally available for such work. Forcing figures that are not linked to the rest of the figure package may be more confusing than useful.

The opening gun in creating a financial model is to construct a sales forecast, then link the expected sales revenues to background a projected income statement. The percentages noted on the dummy statement can be historical or actual, depending on the availability of data. Assumptions of cost items can be made with some accuracy if the farmer-entrepreneur has experience covering actual operations. Obviously, the farmer with a state-of-the-art shop will be able to assess repair costs better than a commercial mechanic only marginally acquainted with any specific farm operation.

The assumptions of, say, a 22 percent cost for printing in terms of sales turned out to be very accurate in the illustration. The buffalo grower, on the other hand, will have discovered his own equation based on hindsight and foresight. Malcolm Beck, the composter, always carried in his head the cost of turning a cubic yard of material, and the wheat grower is more likely to compute accurately the cost of drilling a section, factoring in depreciation and gasoline and repairs with accuracy before any audit can arrive.

ACRES U.S.A. INCOME STATEMENT

	% Revenue
Total Income	100.0
Cost of Sales	
Printing	20.9
Package & mailing	10.6
Art/Photos	.1
Research	.1
Circulation	.3
Royalties	1.3
Conf.: Banquet/Hotel	.3
Outside Services	.0
Manuscript Purchases	.0
Total Costs of Sales	33.5
Gross Profit	66.5
Expenses	
Salaries: Officers	11.8
Labor	18.4
Benefits/Public Relations	.1
Advertising	.7
Office supplies/Postage	7.2
Insurance	.3
Utilities & Telephone	1.4
Rent	2.7
Auto expense	.5
License & Taxes	.0
Darkroom/Shop supplies	.8
Computer	.0
Depreciation	.7
Payroll Taxes	3.1
Subscriptions/Memberships	.2
Legal & Accounting	.6
Contributions	.0
Janitorial services	.5
Office maintenance	2.2
Miscellaneous expenses	.2
Bank/Credit Fees	.0
Travel: 100 percent deductible	.0
Meals: 80 percent deductible	.1
Lodging: 100 percent deductible	.3
Entertainment: 80 percent deduct.	.7
Gas/Park/Toll/Taxi	.0
Total Expenses	52.5
Operating Income	14.0
Other Income	
Cash discount taken	.0
Total Other Income	.0
Other Expenses	
Interest expense	.0
Credit card discounts	.4
Bad accounts/checks	.0
Total Other Expenses	.4
Net Income	13.6

Calculations may never proceed on the basis of wishful thinking and a paucity of experience. No two farm enterprises are alike, even if on the first inspection this appears to be the case. The age of the entrepreneur, the status of his family and its traditions suggest variables that won't compute the same for all people.

The balance sheet can be developed in much the same way. The historical data are equally important in the development of this statement. Indeed, assets often make their appearance on the balance sheet not as a cash expenditure, but as a computation derived with the aid of acceptable accounting principles other systems suffice. One is the accounts receivable turnover period or the inventory turnover period. The rubrics of a balance sheet follow, it being understood that the farmer-entrepreneur will be required to invest assets that come with the enterprise — machinery, buildings, water rights, etc.

These statements are not merely academic niceties, they give substance to the *pro forma* business biography contained in the business plan, and make a necessarily esoteric assembly of projections that become real to one only partially familiar with the grammar on the subject.

Even so, neither the income statement nor the balance sheet erase the need for a cash flow projection.

In an age of inflation, it is useless to cite figures. The frameworks presented here should be enough to illustrate what the narrative in this chapter is all about.

There are several valid methods for constructing a cash flow statement. One system is to take after-tax profits and adding back depreciation and other accounting items that are merely bookkeeping entries and not immediate out-of-pocket payouts. This is not a recommended system, but it can keep the axe from coming down as a liquidity crisis when in fact the operation is solvent.

You can compute the net changes in beginning and ending balance sheets to arrive at the net cash changes. This is a rough way to guard the bucks.

The system I like is tracking cash flow, juxtaposing the results against outflow. The monthly tracking system is to be recommended.

If Eli Pieter, mentioned in the previous chapter, feeds live ducks into the market on a biweekly basis, cash flow almost computes itself. Unfortunately, most farmer-entrepreneur operators have more sporadic inflows. This is one of the reasons farmers develop cash flow disasters. The crop comes in, not quarterly or even semiannually, but at harvest. Miscalculations can cause liquidity crises, and if farm equity is too high, the consequence might be having a lender salivating at the door.

The point here is that the several statements should be linked together, month by month, so that the real picture shines through, like a set of slides in a stereoscope. The running objective is to comply with ratios, break-even points, and calibrations specific to the farm operations.

BUSINESS BALANCE SHEET

Current Assets   Total Current Assets

Fixed Assets
    Automotive Equipment
    Equipment
    Parking area improvements
    Leasehold improvements
    Accumulated depreciation
Total Fixed Assets
Total Assets

Liabilities
Current Liabilities
    Accrued Payroll Taxes
    Accrued Sales Tax
Total current Liabilities
Total Liabilities

Capital
    Capital stock authorized
    Capital stock unissued
    Retained earnings
    Treasury stock
Total Capital
Total Liabilities & Capital

It is almost impossible to make major changes in a model without redoing the structured "seat-of-the-pants" models. While they may serve a Ma and Pa proprietorship, in many cases they simply won't do in the real world of fast-track commerce.

All these exercises falter if great care is not taken in building an assumption statement. It may be stated with little fear of contradiction that an assumption statement rates with the income, balance sheet and cash flow statement in importance to the model. In fact, the first three are based on meaningful assumptions in the first place.

What, indeed, are the variable or out-of-pocket costs? Line items that flow across the several statements have a relationship closer than brothers and sisters. If the relationship is allowed to drift, an important tool is lost.

How is cash on the cash flow statement related to cash on the balance sheet? How do items with the same name or even related names play into each other?

Farmer-entrepreneurs who have devoted their lives to production and little else have a hard time understanding how net income from the income statement and retained earnings from the balance sheet link up. Still they have to understand that retained earnings are derived from net income, not the other way around. If the enterprise is a corporation and dividends are declared, they have to be subtracted from net income and also from ending cash on the cash flow statement.

$$\text{Sales - Expenses = Net Income}$$

This relates to the balance sheet equation:

$$\text{Assets - Liabilities = Net Worth \ (Retained Earnings)}$$

Picture, if you will, a road running from the first equation to the cash flow display, thus;

$$\text{Inflow / Outflows / Dividends}$$

The objective is to know how much money ongoing operations will require, and when it will be required.

The best way to proceed is to set up periods envisioned, namely accounting periods, generally months. Taxes have to be paid that way, and all the government forms conspire to consume an entrepreneur's time at exactly the same time. Periods one to 12 suggest themselves accordingly, assumption statements, with optional data plugged in on that basis, provide the foundation information for balance sheet, period zero (start-up) or number one.

Net sales are developed from data on the assumptions statement (the educated guess) and poured into the income statement, period one.

Once the bookkeeper has been put on the trail, the integrated package forms up with an ease not envisioned earlier. The time periods projected, say the 12 months, form up that way — each one linked to the previous.

The paperwork behind a start-up enterprise, or even one changing its *modus operandi,* cannot expect to find a blueprint perfectly tailored to the envisioned business. Still there are a few rationales and norms that should not be excused from consideration.

Gwynn Garnett, the farmer-author of *PL480* and an astute business-man, once related to me how he projected his therapeutic beef sales. His cattle were grass fed and the market, in addition to being broad spectrum, was basically nearby Washington, D.C. Customers who opted for clean wholesome beef were individuals sensitized to steroids and chemical feed additives in standard grocery store fare. His assumptions were based on experience and pre-start-up traffic before a formal program was launched. His assumption statement forecast sales per annum and then factored out the grower to retailer traffic from locker plant processing. Percent of sales allocated per month came to the following:

Month	Percent
January	4.0
February	5.6
March	3.4
April	5.1
May	8.9
june	7.0
July	4.9
August	2.9
September	4.2
October	8.8
November	19.1
December	26.1
Total	100.0

Gwynn had dollar figures to go with his statement, albeit not for publication. Observation of data over any given period will illustrate growth, a 10 percent objective not being unreasonable, although often difficult to reach.

Projections can give the time-frame and annual gross an assist by suggesting inventory lead times required and peaks and valleys to be expected. Much the same can be said for fixed asset purchases, operating supplies, packaging and services. Even meter postage needs can be anticipated by reading the record in a timely manner.

Depreciation should not wait for an annual statement. In many cases this accounting option, as well as compliance with the miscellany of rules in Prentice-Hall, beckon accounting expertise and employment of an accounting firm for closing and tax preparations is now mandatory for any farmer-entrepreneur, whatever the specialty.

General management principles teach entrepreneurs how to iron out collections in order to anticipate cash flow. This may be necessary if you're a regular supplier to Fresh Fields or restaurant accounts. Some buyer's slow-pay, in effect capitalizing themselves at the expense of the farmer-entrepreneur. How to deal with such problems is properly a matter for business philosophy and accounting. It must be remembered, however, that the farmer-entrepreneur is not in the lending business or structured to be a furnisher of venture capital for wily businessmen who try to live off the capital of others.

An acceptable sequence of ratios of collections achieved, if credit is given, is:

	Collected (%)
0 - 30 days	80
31 - 60 days	10
61 - 90 days	05
90 days or more	05
Total	100

Of course collections are seldom 100 percent, a fact which has to govern the decision to allow credit in the first place. Few commercial enterprises, farm enterprises included, can expect to have regular customers on C.O.D.

The best statements seldom excuse an entrepreneur from having a line of credit — in case. The line to be obtained is set by data emerging from codified statements. Equally important is the minimum balance required, not by the bank, but by the business. There are few things that contribute as much to inefficiency as being put on C.O.D. by suppliers.

Most farmer-entrepreneurs can do a fair job estimating the variable expenses, and they can also compute the fixed costs. If they pause to think about it, they also can realize that variable expenses have to be paid. The farmer owes himself a salary. He has the requirement of computing depreciation, and he probably can deliver on-target, meaningful estimates for everything from phone bills to packaging cartons, with insurance, office supplies and auto gas thrown in for good measure.

Where projections unravel can be called the top line. Up front, it is the most important line. Later, after start-up, other lines can move it over, but when all guns on the firing line start shooting, it's the top line that has to hold fast.

The whiskey maker has to figure consumption figures years in advance. For years Jack Daniel's told its ad readers about the shortage. There was a shortage because either finances or projections to earning the top line, or the top line itself, didn't compute.

Some few organic producers have had top line problems. Either they didn't plan enough to satisfy the ready market, or more likely, the top line estimate was wide the mark. Because of this, separation of the income statement as a side breakout statement from income is indicated.

When the top line departs from the projected norm — either up or down — it can create cash requirements, hence the liquidity crises.

Because of the demeaning approach lenders often extend to small enterprises, I have always operated from a stronger-than-usual cash position, preferring to delay the one expense that is fixed but can be treated as variable — the entrepreneur's own salary.

There is an upper limit to sales that can be handled under the existing structure and cash availability. Greed and getting too big too fast can, and often does, push a healthy entry price into the crises from which bankruptcy flows.

Much the same is true of sales decreases, especially as costs continue to run and cash outflow becomes a raging river.

Building expense estimates in a start-up situation requires its own brand of due diligence. Among the more troublesome items are the following:

Taxes and Benefits. This number can be established by multiplying salaries by the payroll tax (which changes from time to time) and benefit rate.

Rent and Occupancy. These data are simply rent payments plus telephone, utilities and insurance. Each of these items can command its own line, of course.

Advertising and Promotion. The farmer-entrepreneur will have to make a policy decision. Then net sales should be multiplied times, say, two percent of the figure on the sales assumption statement. Indeed, most of the income statement data flow directly from assumptions discussed earlier.

Supplies. General supplies can be computed by subjecting the assumption sales figure to a three-percent multiplier. This may be less, according to the type of office procedures and special requirements.

Depreciation. Although there are several accepted formulas, a straight line system is suggested. Accelerated depreciation sometimes extended to farmers is often counterproductive, especially when heavy depreciation numbers out-pace income. The sources of data here are the balance sheet entries. Accounting services with access to IRS rules and regulations can insert the length of the depreciation period into the equation. The annual depreciation can be divided by 12 for the monthly share of the depreciation expense on the income statement.

Interest Expense. The calculations included here are computed by multiplying the beginning principle balance from the cash flow statement times the annual interest rate, divided by 12 months plus the previous line of credit, if any.

So far I have mentioned the balance sheet in passing, but no real effort has been extended to make its nuances come clear. Simply stated, the balance sheet is a window for observing the financial situation. It is always a mistake to ignore the balance sheet while focusing on the income statement alone. The income statement covers the period in question, usually a month, whereas the balance sheet stops the accumulation of business action for a moment in time. In theory, the opening balance sheet would be a series of titles with zeros dating back to the beginning, the word or idea. In fact it takes up when there is something concrete to record, a cash input, a piece of machinery purchased, whatever. The last balance sheet reveals progress, or lack thereof.

A special caution must be issued at this point. Often smaller enterprises incorporate and issue stock. But they fail to show how or when the stock was paid for. Years later, at harvest, so to speak, the accountants can't find the origin of stock issued. This can result in a capital gains problem that should have remained a molehill, but by then has become a mountain.

The balance sheet might well be part of assumptions at start-up time. A practical point of view, however, suggests solid construction with opaque values. In fact this exercise might be best deferred to the point in time when equipment is obtained, stock is sold and pre-organization activity is underway. As the real start-up day arrives, the balance sheet starts taking on the beauty of a Mona Lisa. Property and equipment becomes a brush stroke. Assets as a whole jump into view and, of course, accounts payable, accrued expenses and long-term debt make an appearance. The point here is that the balance sheet balances.

$$\text{Assets - Liabilities} = \text{Net Worth}$$

The process of bringing figures forward and incorporating data developed during the current period keeps the financial position tidy and net worth real.

Computer literate bookkeepers with suitable programs can spit out accruals with enough detail to fine-tune data to the very day, but this is not necessary much of the time. The business of the farmer-entrepreneur is to make a living and a profit, not to create paperwork government-style. The cash-strong small business is best served by a policy of paying bills promptly, keeping collectibles to a minimum and running a tight production and marketing ship.

This much stated it is now time to return to the business of producing and selling, with tracking no more than a necessary adjunct. Most farmer-entrepreneurs employ bookkeeping help and they usually hire out tax preparations. This is a wise procedure, and yet it often permits the progressive farmer to stumble along in ignorance, too shy or embarrassed to admit that the figures are really mysterious. "I carry my books in my head," is the usual defense. And yet a little study unfolds the mystery. Budgeting a bit of time is the answer and the key to making the records useful.

In running a small business, I have found the daybooks to be most useful. This is not necessarily a diary. It is more a line journal that accommodates transactions keyed to a systematic file. Perhaps a cash register receipt is the journal entry for one day, perhaps other happenings — purchases, memos, treaty sales — all figure according to the type and scope of the business.

Whatever the workaday system, results have to distill toward a trackable bottom line.

CHAPTER 9

A Capital Affair

O nce the farmer-entrepreneur has bolted together basic assumptions with the projected income statement, balance sheet, cash flow suggestions, and sundry schedules necessary for a turnkey operation, the issue of capitalization can be faced with alacrity. Coffee shop advisers will have all sorts of wisdom to offer. *The Wall Street Journal* readers will talk about stock issues, venture capital firms and other approaches. For the most part, these things belong with stories that start with "Once upon a time . . . " as far as the farmer-entrepreneur is concerned. Venture capital firms are not likely to even talk to the likes of Eli Pieter, the duck grower mentioned earlier. And since Eli isn't setting up a King Ranch, the idea of floating stock or issuing junk bonds is equally alien and ruled from both fiction and fact.

A small farm and market enterprise can emerge, homegrown of course, based on sweat equity, family savings and borrowing from friends, but the prospects diminish as the scale of the operation moves upward.

While I was associated with NFO, Butch Swaim and I computed the scale and number of farm bankruptcies. We concluded that the level of farm bankruptcies was governed by the accident of when the farmer was born. The Great Depression of the 1930s was triggered by a public policy that saw basic storable commodity prices cut in half, wheat dropping from the two-dollar level to one dollar a bushel prior to October 1929. For every dollar that aggregate farm income dropped, national income dropped seven-fold. It was not until the mid-1930s that the Roosevelt administration raised the price of corn about five-fold with a loan mechanism and conditions improved somewhat. After that, government programs diluted Milo Reno's militancy and paced the rate of farm bankruptcy. The institutional arrangements for handling farm crops continued to pay the farmer for less than he produced. Those born early enough to have homesteaded or purchased their land for a pittance survived. Johnny-come-lately types went to the wall.

During World War II, farmers who joined the fray via inheritance or investment based on borrowed capital all extinguished debt. Those who came along after a stint in the services took on debt they couldn't pay or service. Inflation came to the rescue for some, others vanished in a pool of red ink that was never diluted by higher farm prices. Ditto for Korean Veterans, Vietnam Veterans and schoolboys counseled by land grant colleges.

Nevertheless, all avenues require examinations, venture firms emerge as storybook sources unless the proposed venture promises obscene profits. Leveraged buy-outs and the type of finance associated with the computer industry are merely distant concepts to the farmer-entrepreneurs. Early stage equity financing, high risk, and inadequate liquidity are fundamentals of the problem. Investment returns must be calculated in terms of

GREEN BENCHES

Two years ago Rick and Marilynn Lynn, Okanogan County, Washington, decided to plant herbs in addtion to their four acres of certified organic soft fruit. They now farm two green benches, raising 19 varieties of herbs, 10 types of pods, 13 grasses, and 18 types of flowers. They aim for three markets: culinary, medicinal and ornamental. In many cases, a plant will fit two or three of the markets. Sage, for instance, can be a spice, a headache remedy, or adorn a wreath.

The dense rows of herbs are harvested in bunches. After drying, the bunches are sleeved in plastic and 25-30 bunches are packed in a case. The Lynns look at their farm as a whole entity of interacting plant populations. There are reasons other than good profit margins to put in a crop, and diversity results in easier handling of pests and weed pressure. "In the end the benefits even out," Marilynn says.

Most of their peaches and nectarines are brokered by an organic fruit marketing company. For herbs, they built up a clientele by "literally going door to door." It's necessary to establish a rapport with the owners of health/natural food stores and florists as an initial step. Once the buyers get to know them, they follow-up by mailing an order list.

The Twisp Farmers Market is convenient for healthy summer retail sales. Population influx to the area is transforming Twisp into a major center of organic commerce. "We usually sell out the Twisp market." Not only does their weekly trip aid their cash flow, but as Rick relates, "It makes you feel good to talk with the people who actually eat the food you grow."

Economically, it's difficult for a small farmer. "It's best to start small with organic farming. For at least three to five years you've got to have a cash flow through an outside income." Rick also has a lawn care business.

capital gains, not dividends.

In Eli's case, the capital required for the planned production and marketing of ducks will have to be raised from "friends of the farm," patient investors interested in penetration of the existing order of things Schumpeter style. Such investors have no takeover plans. They merely expect to ride along for several years and cash in their portfolio when the enterprise is able to buy back the equity. The usual profit for such investors is four to 10 times the capital invested in five to 10 years. Long-term capital gain is the lure, plus the other intangibles mentioned earlier.

Friends of the farm investors frequently contradict business know-how, trade expertise, and financial advice. The bankrolled farm with a plan has head-start status compared to the collateralized loan arrangement.

The real work is finding the source of funds, or having the source of funds find the prospective farmer-entrepreneur.

Withal, finance is at the heart of the successful enterprise. Without it, knowledge, dedication and fortitude come to naught

The role of start-up money varies with the size of the projected enterprise. The organic food movement is full of case reports featuring farmer-entrepreneurs who started their businesses on a shoestring, in some cases capitalizing on consignment inventory, free labor and midnight equity (meaning late hours).

Lifestyle businesses have conjured up thousands of ways for capitalizing the start-up or expansion. The most successful seem to settle for growing slowly, measuring each capital stride the way a scientist measures the nuances of nature.

Fortune 500 employment peaked at 16 million in 1969. Downsizing has become an American phenomenon ever since. The most aggressive of the unemployed victims used savings to capitalize their self-employment, some of them with ventures related to agriculture. Others have used a second job in the family to make the break. Ventures that have failed did so in the main not so much because of a lack of capital, but because the dimensions of planning suffered great shortfalls. The millions and millions of jobs extinguished by company migration to cheap wage areas of the world suggests an explosion in entrepreneurship if employment is to be maintained. Running a tight ship has thus become the name of the game. Turning over the keys to the farm in exchange for capital so far has been the ruin of millions of farmers.

Whatever the route, raising equity is tough work for which thin-skinned people need not apply. The likelihood of being rejected makes the life of a door-to-door salesman sound like a trip to heaven. But for those who stick it out, the rewards confer on life an ultimate exhilaration. Easy access to funding is seldom the lot of the farmer-entrepreneur. Usually people like Bill Gates have them salivating at the prospect of providing capital. After all, computers have become the prime movers of the economy. According to some professionals, the farmer and those who provide the metabolic energy for the human machine are often viewed as so many peasants up to their armpits in mud. The anointed ones enjoy below prime rates, while farmers get a slow grinding turn of the head from side to side from the banker.

That is why cash flow is more important than the codification found on the income statement. That is why solid rapport with suppliers and creditors is always a must. The supplier that allows a bit of time for invoice payment is in fact helping the farmer-entrepreneur with his capitalization problem.

Several suggestions announce themselves:

Try to harness internal sources. This recommendation codifies some of the earlier suggestions regarding start-up funds, growth requirements, and day-to-day working capital. The phrase my dad used was, "Expand on earnings." Another might be, "Don't grow beyond your capacity to absorb the new costs." There might be other sources in times of trouble, but this is not likely because rich brother-in-law types have gone out of style.

Internal funds. These are funds earned and socked away. They are available if a decision is made to use them. They do not dilute working time by making even greater demands on documentation for lender review, analysts or investors. Those who evaluate the worthiness of a venture or expansion thereof have conceptualizations all their own, one of which is Art Carney slowness in reacting to anything. The old saying about money being available when it isn't needed is more real then poetic.

Outside funds. These are funds usually encased in lucite blocks identified as follows:

1. Self-funding (savings)
2. Credit cards
3. Family members
4. Associates and friends
5. Banks and lending institutions
6. Institutions, insurance firms
7. Suppliers
8. Venture investors
9. Private equity investors
10. Public equity investors
11. Commercial paper

Needless to say, these outside sources have a pecking order, the smallest coming first, the larger packages becoming available as the operation reaches maturity.

Personal investments often include office equipment, vehicles, and farm buildings. Brother-in-law loans often intercept problems. The need for letters of intent and documentation can be discerned. The risk involved has to be understood. Professional lenders, such as banks, want collateral, probity in the completion of forms, and airtight papers from

PRESERVING THE VALUES

Western Nebraska is harsh farming country, much of it suited chiefly to grazing beef. But this is not reason enough to shun eco-farming, according to John Coyle. Coyle operates a 1,680-acre spread in the rolling territory north of McCook in Frontier County. Only 640 acres are suitable for row crop prodcuction and require about 100 miles of terraces to preserve the land and guide it into bountiful production.

At one time crops included corn that produced a wholesome red meat, but the art is being priced out of production by subsidized hog concentration camps, a public policy that threatens the elimination of the last of the family farms, and by the toxic technology being taught in the land grant colleges.

John Coyle has translated many lessons of eco-agriculture into programs that control weeds and insects, and make unnecssary the alchemy many farmers have relied on ever since academia made the discovery that pesticide companies have grant money. The linchpin of his program is Agri-Gro, ready carbon in the form of molasses, and few other assists such as fish and foliar products. This general approach has made cutworms and earworms total strangers and kept his wheat crop safe from rust, mildew and other crop destroyers.

John Coyle is pragmatic. He sits atop the Ogallala aquifer, but that lake is 400 feet down, and the high cost of delivering water to irrigated acres has closed down several possible crops. So he produces wheat and cattle — and he specializes in red meat from bulls. Steer meat and meat from cows marbles, a phenomenon uncastrated animals avoid.

Coyle believes the country could be America the beautiful if farmers would cast out toxic technology and if public policy managers allowed profit back into farming. His family of four has left the farm for other employment, causing Coyle and his wife to go it alone. The farm is clean and provides clean food to a nation where it is hard to get anything fresh, clean and wholesome to eat.

While most mainline farmers are lowing their capitalization at the rate of two to three percent a year, the Coyle farm has learned how to hang on while agriculture recaptures its values.

assumptions to the last of the bottom lines. "If he has any assets, I want them in the venture," one banker once told me. "The borrower who risks nothing won't make the business go."

Put this way, the requirement set-up Cheyne-Stokes palpitations simply because the entrepreneur wants a nest egg left over if the venture fails. In the case of lending, conflicts of ideas end up being resolved in favor of the lender. The cost of entry into a new venture is high and failure tends to extract its pound of flesh.

Free money is seldom free. If relatives are involved, then family pressures assert themselves soon enough. Even more important, family and friends may not be good advisers. They also tend to get their way when repayment is not forthcoming in a timely manner, even if there is an "understanding" about such matters. Sometimes these internal battles become intense and vindictive.

Banks create money out of thin air because the law allows them to loan out up to ten times more money than they have. This is accomplished under the fractional reserve principle, the idea being that the run on the banks won't happen in our enlightened age, and there is no likelihood at all that more than a few will demand cash at any one time. Such a mammoth scam simply has to breathe distrust, hence the penchant of bankers to demand twice as much value in collateral as the asked-for loan. This makes the friendly banker a poor source of working capital. Other avenues have to be explored.

Blessed, indeed, is the enterprise that can collect up front for production and services rendered. The composter who spreads the product stands between a rock and a hard place if the client doesn't pay when the product is delivered and the service rendered.

The timing of collections and delivery of payments for open accounts governs the cash position, first, last and always. Inattention to these factors not only allows a liquidity crises to develop, it also shaves away profits off the bottom line.

It will be argued that failure to extend credit costs sales. Failure to pay bills on time has its deficits, one of which is unprofitable time consumption in dealing with irritated suppliers and sudden plunges into C.O.D. status.

Thirty-day credit means one-twelfth of annual sales unavailable for use. Such a posture can be worsened if collections are allowed to run 45 days, or about one-eighth of annual sales. Since the enterprise has to finance its customers, the benefits versus the costs have to be measured and paid for "by adding them to the costs of the beans," Candy Johnson of *Honky Tonk* would say.

The modern development called the credit card has interdicted the bad debt problem for lifestyle and many farmer-entrepreneur companies. A single fact explains the near total applicability of the card to ventures that supply clean wholesome food to a willing cliental.

It is reported, quite accurately I believe, that most of the 40 million serious gardeners in the United States do not consider costs when putting out a vegetable tract. Entertainment, a feeling of well-being, a wish for tomatoes, fruits and veggies not loaded with chemicals, all make the garden worthwhile and prices for inputs a minor consideration.

Something of that order has assumed guiding principle status among consumers of organic food. To customers who think a vegetable is fit food because it looks cosmetically pleasing, purchase of organic food — certified or not — makes no sense at all. Moreover, it is almost impossible to sell such consumers on the proposition that poisons are dangerous and that cheap food now may mean degenerative diseases later on. As with the Irishman who had great faith in God, no proof was necessary, and no proof is enough when people do not think for themselves.

The organic buyer is out there. He or she is constantly at work lining up a supply of food grown in a way that does not pollute food, land or water resources. When they find the eco-supplier, the sales job is complete. So is the collection task that the credit card facilitates. The contribution this instrument makes to cash flow has to be seen to be fully appreciated.

As a business rides down a solvency road, the task of forecasting simplifies itself. Historical records illustrate trends with studied finality. This allows the farmer-entrepreneur to assess environmental changes, whether these changes are legislated or commanded by bureau people, or generated by changes in the total economy. I have deferred discussion of the latter to the last chapter.

The economy can be analyzed by computer models. The psychological and legal climate follows a different drummer, one not clearly understood.

Data published each week in medical journals and the popular press suggest ocean changes for producers and consumers alike. Of all people seeking health care during recent years, nearly half have gone to non-AMA (American Medical Association) health care providers. The advice from almost all of them has been to consider nutrition and the overload of toxicity ingested. No amount of cat-calling and demeaning rhetoric from Centers for Disease Control (CDC) and Food and Drug Administration (FDA) can stamp out this new insight. As a consequence, the few programs for cash sales seek out consumers. This makes it possible to reverse the arrows explained in Chapter 2, which are repeated here:

```
┌──────────────────────────────────────┐
│ ↑    PRICE TO THE CONSUMER    ↑       │
│              TAXES                    │
│      MARKET IN PROCESS COSTS          │
│              WAGES                    │
│          CAPITALIZATION               │
│          RAW MATERIALS                │
└──────────────────────────────────────┘
```

To whom, then, should credit be extended since it affects capitalization so much? The best answer is to evaluate each customer on individual merits. If Eli Pieter supplies ducks to a Chinese restaurant, likely he'll have to extend credit. The individual who walks into the cooler doesn't even expect such a gesture. Credit costs. Employees who deal with credit, taking applications, bird dogging payments, practicing the art of passive aggression, may constitute the biggest salary package other than production workers. Even after terms have been set, litigation is likely to present itself. Few businessmen have time for small claims courts, and fewer still have mastered the rubrics of writing a complaint, filing a traverse, handing off parrot-like answers on interrogatories and depositions, etc. If a case ends up in court, a lawyer has to become involved because an executive can't represent a corporation, and also because an un-lawyered citizen in court causes anger to ooze from every pore of the judge sitting on a highly upholstered swivel chair (called a bench).

The best way to squeeze capital out of the system is to pretend that there is no real competition. There really isn't if the customers you capture are treated well. Few of them lose the faith when they see their friends taken from them or present themselves to the Kervorkian answer because modern medicine hasn't a clue.

Withal, it may be summarized that lesser solutions to the capital problem exhaust themselves quickly if the farmer-entrepreneur attempts to live out of the start-up or expansion enterprise before assumptions are proved out. This reality argues for the investment plans indicated — with suitable instruments being constructed without legal imperfections. An IRS trap can be avoided when the principals exercise due diligence in documenting their entry with major players treated in a special manner, perhaps by issuing preferred stocks or some instrument that sequesters the investment in a manner best calculated to keep the corporate veil from being pierced. If a trust is used, the documentation must be equally impeccable.

A caution must be noted. If special stocks are issued, then Sub-Chapter "S" treatment will not be available since federal law prohibits more than one class of stocks to this business form. Sub-Chapter "S" is attractive if initial start-up losses are expected.

The loan avoids many of the investment complications imposed by tax codes. A note holder has first claim, behind taxes, should an enterprise liquidate.

It is not possible to cover all the ramifications involved here. This capitalization can result in IRS piercing the corporate veil, making the note holder a stockbroker, negating tax advantages believed secure.

Super-caution and legal overkill often attends the formation of business enterprise. In our time, trust has given way to agreements memorialized by documents, as though every dispute would become the court case of the century. Actually the memo is a good idea. People often have memory failure and notes in ink are often enough to resolve the issue. Things like salary schedules, employment agreements, non-compete agreements, all require clear and succinct expression. When the partnership form is used, there is a fiduciary duty of loyalty. Many states hold closely held stock companies to the same high standard.

Not to be overlooked in the matter of stock ownership, in almost all cases there should be an agreement that stock must first be offered to other stock holders in a closely held corporation before selling to an outsider. These few asides are offered because capitalization involves more than funding the money. Capital affairs are seldom done. The death of a principal with provisions of ownership transfer is a case in point. Here the firm loses its valued owner-manager, whatever, and now it has to cough up the money to transfer stock to a capital account, paying out the value of the asset. Such an arrangement ought to be funded by an insurance policy. Operating under a redemption agreement, the company owns the policy and reclaims the stock of the dead holder involved. A second model involves the loss-purchase agreement, with stockholders holding insurance policies on each other. The loss purchase agreement is seldom indicated when more than two stockholders are involved.

A corporation buy-back holds better promise when harvest time arrives. The capital gains basis is now the original investment plus the value inoculated by the insurance payout to the individuals.

There is a bottom line to this discussion. Mere capitalization is never enough. Few think tanks earn their way. They rely on grants, and when they exhaust the grant the tag line almost always calls for more grants.

In the final analysis, the farmer-entrepreneur has to earn his way. New injections of capital are seldom an answer to a model that isn't working. Production and sales are.

Capitalization based on debt is especially lethal. I have been to dozens of farms where "get big or get out" was holy writ. Faced with the reality that the operation is losing, say, two percent of its capitalization per annum, these farmers often harvest advice from Extension, the bank, the chemical company, and this advice says, "You need more acres." I once visited with a Nebraska grower who answered that advice by turning a few grazing acres into an organic plot. "There's my profit," he said, waving his hand. Those few acres made more money than the rest of his 480 grazing acres. His neighbor, already farming a section, took the Extension-banker-chemical company advice, capitalized with borrowed money, and is now gone from the scene, his land handed over to "strong hands," the euphemism for lenders. There is no need to embarass anyone here, so let's move on and consider the business form.

CHAPTER 10

A Business Form

There are few things about businesses that stand alone. A mature sense of values tells us that you can't consider a plan without knowing the form the business organization will take. Similarly, you can't know for certain the best type or form — corporation, partnership or individual proprietorship — without a great deal of investigation. Not everyone will agree, a demurrer I will cover later on.

Most counselors will say corporation, but this is a knee-jerk response, much like the reaction a doctor expects when he taps the patella tendon with a small rubber hammer. Nature accounts for the knee jerk, other stimuli account for the judgment that a corporation is the best form. Let me explain. Since I first saw a TV set all lit up while tripping home from the service after World War II, I cannot remember a time when there was not a series that deified the M.D. physician. Even a Milton Berle joke at the expense of a doctor wasn't smiled upon. The result is that most people hold M.D.s in awe. This deified person orders, he allows, he (now she) puts one on a medicine and takes the business of personal decision making out of the hands of the patient. To question a physician with M.D. after his or her name is unthinkable, a departure from the norm on the order of heresy. As a consequence, people are slow to reject coal-tar drugs, the knife and invasive procedures when safer methods, such as herbs and fresh, wholesome foods would do more to preserve health and recapture the loss of it if invoked on time.

Much the same is true in business. According to some professors, only the corporate form makes sense, even though the corporate shield is pierced like paper-thin armor by the courts. As far as small businesses are concerned — giving the principals very little protection — the form is said to communicate status, confidence and affluence.

True, there are laws, common and statute, that require certain norms of behavior. There are fiduciary duties of disclosure, as an example. This duty of loyalty has superb standing at law, depending on the role an employee or officer plays in that business structure.

A conflict of interest arises when an employee uses business connections to damage the hand that feeds him by helping a competitor or entering the fray as a new competitor using a confidential status to pursue dubious ends.

Many of the same problems exist in the partnership, or in any form that involves multiple personalities. The partnership dies when a partner dies, but this is often true of a closely held corporation, *de facto* if not legal and automatic.

The matter of permits to do business, licenses and compliance with IRS rules and regulations, etc., varies from state to state and status to status, and is not the purpose of this chapter. Suffice it to say that the city or county clerk can supply the answers, including zoning requirements. The Secretary of State in any state will provide the papers necessary for registration, and the sales tax people will positively salivate at the prospect of more revenue entering state and city coffers.

The Sub-Chapter "S" device has been mentioned earlier. The "S" corporation operates exactly like the regular corporation with this exception: "S" changes the formula for tax computation, allowing the principals to be taxed as individuals.

There is also the limited partnership in which a second class of investors are treated more or less like stockholders with limited liability.

The nonprofit corporation is of no consequence to the farmer-entrepreneur except that certifying organizations often take nonprofit status. Nonprofit status is seldom a valid form for publications because that status excuses them from political activity, the right to influence legislation, etc. If such publications become too rambunctious, the long arm of the law makes itself felt soon enough. I have never been able to understand why a newspaper would organize as not-for-profit. I do not think the device has merit for the eco-operation.

The corporation is an artificial person and has to be treated as such by the management and stockholders. Failure to act and present this face to the public is the most common reason the corporate veil is pierced. Failing to use Inc. or Incorporated in designating the enterprise, co-mingling personal expenses and funds, inadequate records, and failure to keep the corporate books replete with minutes and resolutions, all figure in eroding the limited liability the corporate form promises. The public cannot be expected to respect the corporate form if the owners do not.

Here, however, I would like to provide exposition and analysis for a device seldom used to conduct business or preserve assets for a future generation. This is the trust.

There are many types of trusts, the most common being the *inter vivos* trust, or so-called living trust. Any bookstore will sell you a manual on the *inter vivos* trust, always pointing out that its purpose is to avoid probate. This is not the trust of which I write.

I first became acquainted with a real super-rich person shortly after World War II. I don't mean a nodding acquaintance, nor per-

Joe and Dalton Maddox

ORGANIZATION OF A FARM

Formerly dry springs are flowing on the 22,000-acre Maddox Ranch and Joe Maddox says it's due to sustainable land management. The land the Maddox family live and work on has been leased for about 70 years — four generations — and has been worked using Holistic Resource Management (HRM) for the last eight years.

Before incorporating sustainable methods, the management of the Maddox Ranch was counterproductive to healthy land and animals as well as solid finances. Overgrazing and over-resting caused a reduction of plant species and increased erosion. By the time they switched to sustainable methods, the ranch was barren and every rain caused topsoil to erode further.

The Maddox family divided their large area of land into smaller pastures and arranged them in a spoke form around a central watering area. High stock density and a larger number of smaller padocks leads to improved mineral, water and energy cycles. The sheep and cattle graze intensively, leaving behind a large quantity of manure and breaking up the soil with their hoofs. When livestock are moved to the next pasture, the land is poised to absorb the natural fertilizer and begins to produce lush plant life.

Changes in the natural environment on the ranch have been phenonmenal. Beneficial insects and microorganisms have increased. Dozens of new plant species have grown where only prickly pear cacti stood. New flora are great forage for the 30 rams, 900 ewes and lambs, 650 cows and calves and 800 yearlings raised on the ranch. All of these plants help to stablize the soil and prevent erosion. Springs that had been dry due to the lack of soil covers now provide natural water sources.

The Maddoxes avoid costs associated with traditional cattle raising such as growth hormone injections. They spend about $20 per head per year as opposed to the $100 per head per year they spent before the switch. In the future, they hope to garner 18 cents more per pound for their natural beef than the current traditional beef market price.

They have stopped spraying chemical defoliants and no longer use chemical dips for their sheep. They have found that the premium prices paid for naturally grown wool far outweigh the costs of abandoning traditional methods. They plan to team up with an organic cotton farmer to produce high quality organic wool/cotton fabric to sell to clothing and upholstery manfacturers at twice the amount a regular cotton/wool blend commands.

The Maddoxes take their role in their community seriously, on both local and regional levels. They enjoy incorporating the whole family into management of the ranch, and feel that this has a positive effect on their quality of life.

Obviously, such an operation can be set up as a limited partnership, trust, corporation — even as an individual proprietorship — being tuned to the new technology is the determining factor.

sonally friendly, but close enough to pick up vibes I never knew existed. The super-rich are different. They are hard where most of us are soft, and soft where most of us are hard. They keep their trade secrets to themselves and invite into their circles only qualified people, namely those with the credentials of money.

Ferdinand Lundberg, writing in *The Rich and the Super-Rich,* asked, "How has this process been developed through which an entire people have been made penniless after owning at least a few acres of virgin ground?" Unfortunately, he did not stay on for an answer.

The process, upon examination seems clear enough, but for now I will defer an exposition to the last chapter. Not so clear in most informed circles is how mature fortunes escape taxes, if not death, and enable their old money to live on after them.

J.R. Simplot, an Idaho farmer at the start of World War II, found himself seeking this answer. He had developed a system for potato processing just in time to land a contract feeding America's expanding army prior to Pearl Harbor. Income beyond the dreams of avarice arrived soon enough, and behind it the braying sound of IRS operatives wanting a partner's share. J.R. was busy — he was opening new businesses almost daily. Shipping required shipping cartons, and cartons required transport. Product required machinery at the end of the line and fertilizer at the beginning, on and on. J.R. found himself portrayed as an ogre and he did what most people do. He called in the lawyers and accountants and salaried them handsomely. They unlocked a secret held in escrow by the rich and famous — the forwarded funded trust.

I mentioned this trust in an earlier chapter together with suggestions on how to use the instrument for the purpose of saving the family farm from the ravages of capital gains taxes, death levies and forced sale whenever there is a death. The key is simply not to sell, abandon or transfer. The trust, if properly set up, lives on. Co-trustees simply vote to replace the departed co-trustee, and the farm is never forced into liquidation if the trustees decree otherwise. This *Guide* will not provide the instruments needed to accomplish this purpose, that being the role of a specialist.

My own trust is refurbished by a will which includes the following language, "I give all my estate and property to the co-trustees serving at the date of my death in such capacity under the terms of that certain living trust, all of said estate and property to be held and administered according to the terms of said living trust." The Simplot Trust had all children as co-trustees. The death of a child or co-trustee merely results in one remaining co-trustee replacing the missing co-trustee.

A clearer picture of the device can be had by thinking of the sale of Rockefeller Center in New York. When the Japanese purchased the center, there was no transfer of property, no activity at the Register of Deeds office, no government involvement. Simply stated, a group of trustees got up out of their chairs, and a new group of Japanese trustees sat down. All other arrangements were outside the purview of transfer mechanisms usually fatal in an age of inflation.

Suppose the farmer-entrepreneur puts $100,000 into his trust. His wife and four children are co-trustees and one is selected as manager. Taxes on the earnings of the trust — say interest from T-bills or other investments — are taxed under the trust's tax number. The co-trustees all have access to the checking account, technically money can be drawn out, but no income tax is paid on these accounts. Now you see how the rich and famous get even richer.

Obviously, such a trust could be used to run the farm enterprise. Many producers and second-tier in the multiplier pyramid do. They file 1099s and W-2s on wage earners or commission salesmen. The trust pays its earnings taxes. It has no franchise regulation fee, but generally speaking it meets the obligations of a business even down to complying with fire and zoning codes.

This trust, with a will attached, makes it possible for all property not titled over to the trust to pour into it upon death of a founding co-trustee. The surviving co-trustees do the pouring. They do the bills of sales, make the assignments, etc.

There are problems just the same. Much like the end products of TV programs that deify doctors, most people can't stop themselves from running to lawyers. They have been conditioned to do this and respond to a guiding hand. The lawyers respond; "I can't do this. I need court authority."

The authority of the trust and the co-trustees can move titled property; much of the corporation's double taxation can be avoided, and public disclosure of private business can be sidestepped. From my chair, it is incredibly wise to run a small business this way.

Why, then, do farmer-entrepreneurs seek the dubious comfort of conventional wisdom rather than uncommon good sense? Perhaps Bob Livingston can provide a clue.

Conventional wisdom is based on confusion and disinformation. It has a crowding-out effect in our thought processes, and inquiry is stifled. In other words, conventional wisdom programs us to reject any information or thought not in harmony with our preconditioning and experience. It is called cognitive dissonance.

Max Plank, a Nobel physicist and colleague of Albert Einstein, has handed out an equally poignant comment for our consideration:

A new scientific truth does not triumph by convincing its opponents and making them see the light, but rather because its opponents eventually die, and a new generation grows up that is familiar with the idea from the beginning.

I memorized these lines some 50 years ago and pass them on, sans source other than a college text now forgotten.

I have developed the general idea mentioned here simply because most people won't believe that a business can be run that way, *sans* double taxation, and with special benefits for the founding fathers. No one cites Federal 9134003 which allows the pre-funded trust to feed the family out of the trust. The intermediate bottom line is that if you're not going to be competent and courageous, you'll spend most of your years in abject poverty.

Realistically speaking, the professional corporation is of small value to the chiropractor or veterinarian. His interest would be better served with the package described here, for it would make unnecessary transfers, conveyances, or movement of property. Merely changing the co-trustee

CONSUMER INVOLVEMENT

Within one year of startup as a CSA-style marketing system, Baird Family Farm, Pickens, South Carolina, experienced success, grew and made big plans for the future. Dick left his job to become a full-time farmer, literally building the farm from forest land. Originally 15 acres, they now have 85 acres — most still wooded — and produce a wide variety of food certified organic by CFSC.

Beyond simply organic, the Bairds grow biodynamically and seek to increase the diversity of their farm, constantly adding crops and animals to the mix. Currently they grow blueberries, with the plants pruned higher than usual so goats can graze the orchard floor. "We try to keep the mower out and the goats in. Last year we only mowed twice," Dick Baird says. They are pasturing 85 chickens, all layers, in Salatin-style pens, although they hope to expand to at least one cycle of broilers this season. Their three acres of vegetables feature some 50 varieties. They also milk five dairy goats.

In the first year of this CSA, they sold 50 shares, mostly to residents of nearby Greenville, Clemson and Anderson, South Carolina. These towns circle the farm about 35 miles out. They pick and deliver twice weekly, with one delivery to a Greenville drop-off point and one delivery to the Clemson/Anderson area. With the recent addition of 3.5 acres of bottomland from an adjoining farm, they expect to double membership in one to two years.

They have completely designed and built the farm by hand, including an irrigation system fed from a creek running through the heart of the farm's bottomland. They also have a spring that originates on the farm which enabled them to add a hand-dug pond — both for "hanging out" and to harvest rainbow trout for CSA members. They recently planted chestnut trees, a crop Baird thinks other farmers should look at. There are only 500 acres of chestnut trees in America, with each acre yielding 3,000 pounds of nuts per year. They plan to erect a 30- by 100-foot greenhouse as well.

Of all the mistakes they've made, the worst was machine clearing one area. "That area is the one we're still having trouble bringing into balance."

Their holistic methods of farming translate to their own lives as well. Beth home-schools son Lucas as toddler Taz looks on.

Here is a case of growing the farm from the ground up. For now, the individual proprietorship will do. Consumer involvement in the farm makes its own suggestion.

accomplishes the same purpose when an enterprise is involved. Once a farm or a practice is ensconced in the name of a trust of this style, the entity lives on *ad infinitum*. The IRS won't bother a trust that pays its taxes.

An attorney named Bill Williams was one of the few trust experts with experience in setting up a super-rich trust, the kind used by the rich and famous. He cut his teeth in the game as an attorney for the Terteling Company owner, a specialist in the earth moving business and a drinking buddy to J.R. Simplot. Trust intelligence was passed that way, and fortunes made building Grand Coulee Dam did not elude N.L. Terteling who had corporations to sell Caterpillar tractors, but trusts owned the stock. Dividends flowed into the trust.

The conduit for this information, generally, is the social club. When you see a pileup of personal jets at Sun Valley, you can bet your bottom dollar something besides the football game is being discussed, and there won't be any professors there either. The attorney who installed this trust among the holders of big money in Idaho learned the rudiments while working with super-rich clients, and Bill Williams picked up the foundation elements while managing eight of the trust entities.

"I don't believe it," remains the impediment that keeps common folk from helping themselves. They might as well say, "I refuse to think for myself. I must have the imprimaturs of the lawyer or the doctor, or I won't set foot on their territories."

Napoleon once "marveled at what men would do, and the suffering they would endure," so that he would pin a medal on them. He would not need to marvel at all were he to witness open heart surgery, or devastation of family fortunes by attorneys, and a willingness to endure it, all by people who, frankly, have been conditioned to endure.

The problem is that often the farm enterprise will not endure the form of organization imposed on it. The old homestead farm is a sitting duck under conditions of inflation. Here's a farmer who bought the farm during the 1930s at $10 an acre as a young boy. He dies. Capital gains taxes swing into gear. Estate taxes, income taxes, and all the rest soon command some 65 percent of the value, and heirs are sent packing.

I have pointed out the capstone propositions identified above, only to be told, "No, that won't work." Like Jonathan Winters who, in *It's a Mad, Mad, Mad, Mad World,* insisted upon being told about Smiler's treasure, "Everybody has to pay taxes, even crooks pay taxes." Of course that is correct. But it is entirely legal to plan a business and estate to take advantage of the laws that have been written for our benefit.

Whatever the form a business organization takes, its framework should permit orderly growth. Some enterprises are set up on a growth plan that ratchets up production as sales indicate. In publishing, histories of journals that start as quarterlies and then monthlies, finally moving up to biweekly and weekly status are legion. Much the same is true of farm enterprises that crossover into the multiplier sector of the economy. Some merely reclaim middleman functions taken off the farm by the march of industrialization. Others offer the market something so unique that sales pull up production behind them. Usually the form of organization does not stand in the way, but it can, and this should be assessed as a part of the business plan.

No form of organization exempts the farmer-entrepreneur from laws covering social security, workmen's compensation and legal requirements mentioned and discussed earlier and to be discussed later on. These reminders are only peripherally a form of the business consideration, and yet they demand analysis and analogy as the mix jells into a solidified form. Workmen's compensation is burdensome, to be sure, but it is offset by a lifted burden of litigation in exchange for payment in case of job-related injury. The form of organization does not include liability coverage, that being an expense matter. Nevertheless, a farmer-entrepreneur who allows the public on his farm should err in the direction of safety by carrying a substantial liability policy.

A concise review now may be in order.

1. *The Sole Proprietor.* This form is what you are if you simply go into business. The one owner is held liable for the firm, its activities and its debts. The risk of loss is entirely on the shoulders of the proprietor looping all of his or her assets into the losses if any.

2. *Partnership.* In this business form two or more people are co-owners who share profits and losses. They are equally and separately liable for debts and activities of the business. A poor judge of character should never go into a regular partnership. The death of a partner terminates the business.

3. *The Corporation.* An artificial person and the franchise of a state extending limited liability to its owners. It is taxed on earnings, and dividends are not subtracted before the bottom line is achieved. The corporation can elect to payout taxed earnings or hold them for expansion.

4. *Limited Partnership.* A business form that allows one class of investors to enjoy limited liability.

5. *Professional Corporation.* A business form available to accountants, architects, doctors, etc., albeit not to professional farmers. The form allows for certain tax advantages and limited corporate liability. It does not protect a doctor or lawyer from being sued.

6. *Sub-Chapter "S" Corporations.* A special form that allows closely held corporations to be taxed as individuals. This form has no other advantages.

7. *The Trust.* As described above, it permits co-trustees to operate a business on behalf of a family, prevent property transfers and in effect avoid estate transfers. It is a natural for a family trying to keep capital gains and estate taxes from consuming the estate upon the death of a principal, and yet permits the farm to operate as a business.

In a way, the form determines the plan and, equally, the plan determines the form.

CHAPTER 11

The Promo Package

Right or wrong, the customer is the operational reason for being. Since the principles entertained here are not target specific, they can be invoked to fit the situation whether the farmer-entrepreneur sells at wholesale, retail or both.

Products from the farm are generally styled non-technical. This does not preclude the new or expanding enterprise from falling into the product orientation trap. This trap is usually lethal in the hands of a fussbudget or windbag, one incapable of empathy with the buyer, not that of a soil scientist, clinician or lecturing professor. This can prove difficult, especially when the customer has only recently tiptoed into the arena that is the subject of this book. Customer orientation not product orientation. The line can be fine. The first approach tends to say, "Here are foods, grains, meats, whatever, that fill needs, either those of a retail customer or down-line requirements of other sales enterprises." Endless prattling about esoteric features or proprietary advantages embodied in the product may be a sales killer as is the wrong answer in a court of law.

Much the same can be said of the one sin almost all farmers commit with reckless abandon, namely production orientation to the detriment of all else. Most farmers would rather produce and transport the product to market, which in fact is what they do, ending their tale of woe with, "What'll you give me?" Often they lose sight of the market's wishes entirely, producing oats, corn, beans, wheat and other storable commodities with hardly a thought of price or profit until it is quite late in the game.

Management of costs often becomes a prime concern, cross-infecting peer pressure with production reality to the detriment of the bottom line. This foible results in a lot of second-hand machinery reaching the market, but it often does not square well with the demands of a profitable bottom line.

These several considerations seem to warn against the aim of the enterprise, to sell. It is not necessary to belabor the fact that selling is but a simple entry in a marketing scenario. We seem to want to convert the fruit of the farm into cash, and yet we endure the warning that the customer's needs come first. They do, of course. The hard sell thus becomes a self-defeating method, and forever condemns the shyster and blackjack operator.

Probably the most useful approach for the farmer-entrepreneur is integrated focus. This means everyone has to learn how to answer a telephone and convert incoming messages to meaningful memos or orders. The yard worker who is rude or pretends a speech impediment while rattling off information so that it can't be understood is a *de facto* saboteur, whether the farm owner or friends of the farm know it or not. The bookkeeper can annihilate a customer-seller relationship by talking down to corporate clients, even bill collectors or sales reps in the trade. The curt refusal to talk to a reporter or radio microphone can be equally chilling to the area in general.

In short, the farmer-entrepreneur has to separate the love of production from the demanding role tradition has accorded it. These few notes are presented more as an aside, not as a scolding to those who have not thought of the matter in the past.

Aside or prelude, the way is now clear for travel down the marketing road. The goals outlined in the several financial papers discussed earlier are not never-never land targets, rather measures for success that sound planning makes possible. Sales as used here should be profitable sales.

Traps to be avoided, goals to be reached, bottom lines to be etched in stone, all call for an image under which rules and procedures can be housed.

The farmer-entrepreneur, like the *Bible* salesman, has to believe in his heart that every human being can be a potential customer. And I think I have explained that the impediment to such goal attainment is lack of wisdom. A brief orientation into the subject simply will not suffice. Use of clean, wholesome foods for health maintenance can't be advertised into being, nor can they be browbeaten into subjects. It has been said that people take leave of their senses as a group. They come to their senses one at a time. Consumer ranks are full of people who actively seek the products of the eco-farm. When they find a source of supply — Bingo! — the steady customer comes into being.

Nevertheless, the new food provider of which I speak is positioned in a highly competitive and saturated market. That is why it becomes necessary to create a differentiated image for the farm or farm-related enterprise.

HERBS & FLOWERS

Jennifer Erickson hails from New Zealand where she was trained as a horticulturalist and learned about biodynamic farming. When she married Steven Erickson and ended up at a 6,000-foot elevation farm in Coalfille, Utah, she realized the way to farm there would be to grow frost-hardy herbs. Together, the Ericksons grow culinary and some medicinal herbs as well as make compost for sale in their region.

They follow biodynamic principles and fertility management is accomplished through cover crops, crop rotations and composting. They use annual or semi-annual rotations and biodynamic preparations. They have had success peppering for weed control, especially with quackgrass. A garlic and cayenne spray works well on aphids and a soap and beer spray gets rid of box elder bugs. Flea beetles are another story and they're still looking for the answer to that one. Foliar feeding is seaweed and fish.

Beneficials are so abundant, Steve says, "We can't even identify them all." There are lacewings, ladybugs, praying mantis, birds and bats. Some species on the property are unusual for an elevation so high. The rotations and cover crops also help in pest control.

Culinary herbs are marketed to restaurants, distributors, grocery stores and to an on-farm store. The Ericksons deliver to a 60-mile radius of customers. Medicinal herbs are generally contracted. Flowers grown on the farm are sold to florists as cut flowers or dried flowers and are also marketed at the store. Steve and Jenny have also started some value-added production such as an herb vinegar, frozen pesto, and a catnip fish for the local kitties.

The compost is done on-farm and biodynamically using manure from a local dairy farm. Steve says, "It's been a neat operation for us. We've influenced the dairy farm to change some of their practices, and it's been a good education for both of us."

When asked what got them in to herbs, he replied, "We heard Richard Alan Miller speak when we attended an *Acres U.S.A.* Conference in 1984."

Biodynamic is rapidly becoming a household word in the U.S.A. As an image maker it is a natural, one perfectly suited to the development of a bottom line.

Friendly mailing lists can be used to create or expand the image. We tend to think of image in terms of a logo or symbol. This is not enough. In Century 21, the computer and computer literacy are often mandated, seldom excused. The very existence of such capability creates its own list of suggestions.

Obviously, the farmer-entrepreneur has a vital need for his customer list, replete with details to be gathered without becoming invasive or obnoxious. The customer will give up his name and address without objection, usually. But when the quest for details reaches into phone numbers, age and anniversary dates, the simple sale becomes an interrogation. It takes art and diplomacy to gather in details and heads-up attention to use details properly.

The best friendly list is the one you compile for yourself. The best checklist on customer relations is the one you discern when the entire farm, sales and shipping department, is viewed from afar, then close-up. Certain questions have to be asked and answered.

Item 1. Is there a system or procedure for collecting vital information on the needs of your customers?

Item 2. Is it possible to go out of the way for customers with special needs, packages, etc.?

Item 3. Is orientation of all those associated with the farm on customer relations a going concern?

Item 4. Is contact maintained with customers, say on special sales days, or special personal days such as anniversaries and birthdays?

Item 5. Have you developed a system for converting occasional customers to steady customers?

The several hundred farmers used to background this book have revealed a staggering number of approaches to the business of passing the word. The most successful have made the points in Chapter 3 their own, especially the one that asks farmer-entrepreneurs to do their own thinking. One and all agree that consumers have market requirements, some of which are subjective. Certain impulses to buy organic, for instance, are not controlled to any great extent either by customers or competitors. These are economics, social and what is nowadays called "politically correct." For example, newspaper reports on vitamins cause some people to avoid natural foods, others to do just the opposite. This is not to suggest that buyers of fresh and wholesome food from the eco-farm are contrarians, rather that they have a higher level of intelligence and can make judgment without reference to approving authorities. Finding such customers is doubly difficult in harsh political environments.

First, superior food products must be purchased and diffused through the population. When this happens repeatedly, so called word-of-mouth takes over. In a sense, organic foods have the attributes of new products, albeit not fad-type entries into the market. Fads — say shoe laces with hearts or other card deck symbols — must be considered a fad, like the hula hoop. Word-of-mouth and news exposure takes them to dizzy heights and then the gods of the markets allow them to plummet like a hot potato.

The steady growth of the organic movement over the past 25 years puts products of the eco-farm into the category described by Joseph Schumpeter as changes of institutional arrangements.

The opener for a start-up farm enterprise has to be awareness, then interest, then evaluation, trial and routine purchase. Customer progress through these several stages signals how well the objectives of the business plan are being met.

Eco-farmers, CSA co-operators, secondary suppliers such as organic grocery stores, all have tried the standard approaches in merchandising, and many have added ideas of their own. The size of the operation dictates the range of possibilities.

Chris Weick, the Texas free-range chicken grower mentioned earlier, merely calculates order forms and allows the word to circulate. Yellow page ads, newspaper ad space, and TV and radio spots are much too costly for the one-man operation with only temporary help. This means more subtle uses of the media must be employed.

Possibly the greatest vehicle for making a community "organic conscious" is the talk show. There are hundreds of these reactive radio programs. In some areas programs identify themselves as organic, as is the case in San Antonio where Manuel Flores answers questions on gardening without poisons. Other such shows in the several major cities of Texas — notably Howard Garrett in Dallas — sell the sizzle, and leave it up to the farmer-entrepreneur to tap the living river of inspiration these shows have become. Fred Clark advertises on a Dr. David Beaulier's health show in Kansas because radio time is sometimes affordable for garden suppliers and even farms. The point here is that good shows should not be allowed to die the minute they go off the air. Tapes should be kept available for circulation and replay.

Much the same is true of the feature story. Local papers like to feature successful organic farms. Such stories should never be allowed to die. Reprints are cheap and permission is almost always available for the asking. Carl Garrich, the Paragould, Arkansas organic rice producer, kept a reprint concerning his production system and sales program with Erehwon alive for 20 years or more, distributing it whenever the situation allowed.

Hanging notices and flyers on bulletin boards is another innovative way to announce the availability of products from the biologically correct eco-farm; especially if there is a connection with someone in the business, building, or church involved. Printing should always be sprightly, clean and simple. Computer-generated copy is quite satisfactory for this purpose.

The best way to get the most bang for the buck in printing is to exhibit some knowledge of the grammar of the subject. For reasons that may seem trivial, printers escalate the price of a run when they believe they have a novice on their hands.

The mix called promotion has several component parts, not the least of which is pricing. Pricing is neither the small steel pin on which the gate called promotion swings, nor is it the price mover for the farmer-entrepreneur. It is, however, a calculated risk/goal, and calculation does indeed require calculation.

Pricing seems to trouble farmer-entrepreneurs. It has always been handled by others — by those wizards of the Board of Trade who "discover" prices, for instance, and by the auction block or "What'll you give me?" tradition.

Fortunately education and the worsening reputation of regular grocery store offerings, with well-researched toxicity levels and health threatening quality to offer, are elevating organiculture to a price worthy posture. Prices for Arkansas and Alabama chickens have little impact on prices people are willing to pay for chickens grown in a humane way. "Get the price in the supermarket, then double it," often has been the advice to organic producers.

A sound approach to pricing has to counter costs in production, the dedication of a clientele and the quality of demand. Costs merely estab-

FIRST MAGNITUDE STATUS

Bob Birkenfeld, of KGB Composters and Farm, Nazareth, Texas, is certain that his family and his land have benefitted since he switched to sustainable farming. Bob went organic because he felt dissatisfied with the relationship he had with his land. Birkenfeld's goal today is to keep his land healthy and productive, and to provide well for his family.

Born into a farming family, Birkenfeld owns 187 acres of land, 57 acres of which are cultivated. Birkenfeld helps operate a 3,500-acre farm and KGB Composters with two of his brothers using integrated pest managment (IPM) and compost as fertilizer. All of the land has been chemical-free since 1990, and virtually all of it is certified organic through the Texas Department of Agriculture's Organic Certification Program.

KGB Composters and Farm is not only one of the largest certified organic farms in Texas, it is one of the most diversified. On the 2,880 acres in production, 480 acres are planted with cotton, 2,000 with wheat, 280 with corn, and 120 with grain sorghum. Birkenfeld uses ladybugs, trychogramma wasps and green lacewings for pest control and controls weeds through manual cultivation. Although the cost of hiring six farm hands may seem high, Birkenfeld is adamant that the increase in labor costs is more than offset by reduced chemical costs and increased crop value. Birkenfeld commands premium prices for organically-grown cotton.

When he found himself dissatisfied with available fertilizers, Birkenfeld decided to start a

composting business and began producing compost for area farmers and ranchers.

Birkenfeld's marketing methods are as diverse as the crops he grows. He has developed a mailing list to help him market the compost and has also begun to look outside the United States for potential markets, hosting interested industry representatives from as far as Japan at his farm. Birkenfeld says, "Markets for organic produce are finally starting to come around and word-of-mouth travels fast."

Bob Birkenfeld's long-term goal is to achieve self-sufficiency on his land. He wants to pare down his acreage to just under 400 acres, providing for his immediate family's needs while working on a simpler lifestyle including more time for his wife and children. He doesn't want to let his work take him away from what he sees as the most important thing for his family — quality of life. Bob Birkenfeld sees sustainable agriculture as a key element in achieving this quality of life.

In an area notorious for chemical input, Birkenfeld's image has elevated organic to first magnitude star status. Consumers are taking notice.

lish a floor. The objective is cost — plus a reasonable profit. Again, simple arithmetic has to be the final arbiter.

Farmer-entrepreneurs are not as likely to be capitalized as were the supermarket chains of the 1930s that swept a more efficient grocery system from the field.

There are other considerations — break even pricing, for instance. This system expects total recovery in the shortest possible time with the rest of the product quickly expendable or subject to final sale or close-out status. This probably isn't the way to run a specialty enterprise, and organic food production first, last and always has to be considered "specialized."

Target pricing is much like the above, except that the profit level is targeted regardless of any break-even objective. Demand and hoped for customer stampedes are too seat-of-the-pants for this approach, which in any case takes on the aura of being scientific. A price computed on the basis of the target objective expects to wash away costs and survive with a healthy bottom line regardless of quantity sold.

Never an option for the farmer-entrepreneur is the "going price." This approach is tantamount to letting the alternative supplier set your prices. Commercial legends are full of case reports in which a well-capitalized supplier cuts prices until weaker entrepreneurs are exhausted, then drop out. Buying into this ploy keeps the farmer-entrepreneur about one step away from perpetual penury. If prices don't work out on paper, they won't work out in business.

Pricing, much like promotion, simply has to be a part of the selling plan. But it can never be the loss leader giants invoke, not when the business is "lifestyle" and the capitalization is on a frayed shoestring.

Communication with an audience implies the existence of something to be communicated. The product — yes. The price — yes. Publicity — yes. The most effective communication appears to be reputation and the symbol of the reputation, the logo.

The trade press generally is eager to receive feature stories about the new farm enterprise. *Acres U.S.A.* has filled its pages with success stories for over 30 years. Local and club newsletters love well-written news — feature material for instant use, and such material can then be kept alive as reprints. Much the same is true of expository material that tends to support the reason for being of the organic approach, although such items are harder to place. They are easy to find and are kept in circulation for the purpose of consumer education. The key is to think in terms of the newspaper or media needs. Two hundred to three hundred words is an ideal length.

Creativity is "think for yourself in high style form." All the media can be found in the local library. Large glossy photos, not small color snapshots, are raw meat for media, except for TV exposure which uses color.

Community service often permits entry to the media — a special turkey, if that is what you produce, can be spared for charity, and so on.

Several cautions should be kept in mind when trying to reach audiences.

1. The cost must be assessed.

2. The ability to actually reach the target audience rather than just numbers.

3. The message from the farmer-entrepreneur is generally complicated, and requires Ernest Hemingway simplicity to survive and reach more base.

4. A reactive audience must be dealt with, both favorable and unfavorable, and an ability to handle this credibility chore is mandatory.

Costs for the first three named above are usually very low. The cost of the personal touch is high simply because salaried help is high. It takes eyeball contact to make the most of a sales possibility. Indeed, the personal touch wins in all areas, especially in delivering a complicated message and maintaining credibility and rapport.

Direct mail has not been given broad spectrum attention because of its high cost. Once the open sesame to the target audience, it clamors for attention amid mountains of slick junk. The printing costs are not alone in running up debts. Postage has become obscene. With much mail now going the FAX route, postal delivery seems destined to serve only papers, magazines and advertisement broadsides. Such a prognostication is a little intense, to be sure, but it points up the need to assess mail communication diligently. Cold canvassing on behalf of the farm enterprise and organics is probably too costly. If the list is a good one — say, previous customers, current customers, attendees at special meetings, then a simple black and white mailer, nothing fancy, is more likely to exhibit pull than four-color foldouts on high-gloss paper.

There is a bottom line even at the halfway house in the package called financial papers. It is simply this. Everything noted here has to be flashed back to the final revised plan discussed earlier, then carried forward into day-to-day operations.

The focus of the profit factor that escapes the farmer can be identified by considering the division of the food dollar. Fully 69 cents of the consumer's food dollar are spent for so-called middleman functions — distribution and processing. This is the area for concentration of efforts to recapture former farmer-entrepreneur functions. Direct distribution holds promise, but it may not be the entire answer. Nor is transportation to be lightly assessed. There are economies of scale and function in both areas that require diligent study. In classical economics, it is assumed that inefficient middlemen eliminate themselves, with entrepreneurs doing away with inefficiency whether it is institutionalized or not.

Non-store marketing has taken its place with innovations such as mail order, door-to-door or route selling and delivery. Catalogs cost money. So do route vehicles and special delivery.

Setting up question marks should not be taken as dismissal of an idea. The idea proposed for a vehicle to traffic across an entire state for the purpose of delivering packaged meat might be dismissed by some, yet this very idea has been made to work in South Dakota, and is being considered in the upper peninsula of Michigan. Some customers have never seen the delivery system work, being away from home when it arrives. Trust between producer and customer is so great, and the demand for clean meat protein is so great, a hidden key permits entry so a freezer can be filled. In South Dakota they call it "the Goosemobile," possibly because it lays the golden egg for both consumer and farmer-entreprneur.

Factor these considerations into the equation and it becomes obvious that the expenses of the middleman cannot be removed entirely by becoming a middleman. But when the farmer-entrepreneur becomes his own middleman, and does the job efficiently, he starts diluting the market's penchant to pay everyone except the farmer, often letting the primary producer hold the bag.

CHAPTER 12

Sales & Marketing

Several years ago, in connection with the 25th anniversary year edition of *Acres U.S.A.,* I started assembling case reports on successful eco-farmers, most of whom qualified under almost any organic certification program. The publication scheme called for vignettes — two per state, for all fifty states, with special attention to the full package under consideration: production and marketing. From Alabama to Wyoming, the case reports stacked up, and in time I was able to distill reflections on what was going right and what was going wrong.

Up front, readers met up with an interesting on-farm store. The store came into being shortly after Alyce Birchenough and Doug Wolbert of Sweet Home Farm in Alabama got married. Doug gave Alyce a cow, and the cow gave Alyce milk, after which Alyce proceeded to make cheese. The numbers are germane because they illustrate the anatomy of new wealth entering the system. Grass became milk, and 100,000 pounds of milk turns into 10,000 pounds of homemade cheese, all of it sold at the farm's store near Alberta, Alabama.

First came the idea and then a few token resources were put into place. Next came the qualification requirement exactly as outlined in this *Guide*. The couple read everything they could find on cheese making. Alyce enrolled in a cheese-making course to learn the trade. A lot of experimentation followed before the couple was ready to add successful retailing to their farming operation. In that process they learned more than technology. They learned about markup, discounts, and the role of business nomenclature that often eludes primary producers because they go as far as the door, but do not enter.

Experimentation is the name of the game. Wolbert says, "I do everything in experimental stages." He uses many varieties of clovers and gras-

EARTH CARE FARM

Earth Care Farm is a 23-acre diverse, Charlestown, Rhode Island, certified organic farm. Farming methods are looked upon as a lifetime process. The Merner family, field and business managers, and 11 developmentally disadvantaged people use the farm in growing crops, maintaining facilities, marketing, and beautifying the property with landscaping activities.

Soil health is the foundation upon which all efforts are built. Beginning at first with an acid soil, low in organic matter and deficient in nutrients, compost has been applied for many years to bring the soil to an excellent state of fertility. Earth Care has a well-managed three-acre compost pad with swales, berms, and retention ponds to control and prevent run-off. In cultivating the three acres of annual vegetables, herbs, flowers, and perennial berries, weeding is done with wheel hoes, hand hoes, living mulches, and conventional mulches.

Being off-the-beaten path, an on-farm roadside stand is not feasible. Marketing is primarily wholesale to supermarkets, produce stores, health food stores, restaurants, and farmers markets. Earh Care sells organic vegetables, herbs, berries, Christmas trees, and compost. In 1994, the Rhode Island Northeast Organic Farming Association (NOFA-RI) started a marketing cooperative with a dedicated coordinator, and Earth Care Farm will participate.

Specialty niches include compost production and sales, wholesale distribution of natural/organic fertilizers and soil amendments, and natural/organic lawn care and landscaping services provided off-farm by The Organic Landscape Company. The Merners think that without the related businesses it would be very difficult to survive as a small New England farm only selling wholesale.

At Earth Care Farm, the people feel that one of the greatest benefits of their organic agricultural practices is that it keeps them in touch with traditional values and awakens an understanding and respect for the spiritual nature within all life.

Michael Merner

es. Once a year he applies 1.5 tons of poultry manure as fertilizer. Recently he tried mushroom compost on part of the field, peanut on another, because he worries about the build up of metals with poultry litter. He limes in the fall for winter crops and does not fertilize all summer. "Im managing the pasture for my dairy," Wolbert says. "I'm not managing the clover, I'm managing the dairy production, the curd."

As for advice, Doug stresses marketing. "Farming is one thing, marketing is another. The way to get the best of it is to do both jobs. This is where sustainable agriculture comes in. We're small eough to be able to handle and market our own products."

The idea of making a run through the states picked up steam. It soon became apparent to me that each vignette not only encapsulated astounding technologies, but also philosophical insight.

Many of these reports illustrate the sophistication growers exhibit in bringing themselves to that part of the plan that separates production from entry into the multiplier sector of the economy, the area in which farm profit seekers often flounder.

In surveying and reporting on several hundred eco-farms, I have turned up several approaches to the business of reabsorbing middleman functions, *ergo* profits. I do not suggest that farming smart and treating the soil system like something that belongs on a jeweler's scale isn't a first consideration. Most of this new breed of farmers like to keep it simple. This means they sell direct, and if their markups are erratic at times, they justify their pragmatic procedures as necessary, effective and profitable. Dave Wright of Palmer, Alaska simply takes his produce to the farmer's market at Fairbanks. Usually visited by 10,000 people each week, consumers practically inhale what he has to offer, his quality vegetables are that outstanding. His tag, Harmony Acres, is enough to bring all the customers he can handle to his stand.

Don't tell Dave Wright he can't do something because he is going to prove you wrong. When he was told he couldn't grow squash in Alaska, he went right ahead and produced a big variety of winter squash. When he was told you couldn't compost in Alaska, he got his up to 160 degrees and it breaks down in three months. Dave started Harmony Acres basically growing vegetables — including broccoli, cauliflower, potatoes, carrots, beets, lettuce, radish, tomatoes, strawberries, raspberries, celery, onions and garlic — on two acres of land.

The growing season begins with May planting and usually ends in September. Because you can't use traditional crop rotations in Alaska, Dave pays careful attention to his soil. He uses bedding and blood from the local slaughterhouse as part of his compost. When he is plowing over a field of grass, he sprays on blood and lets the microbials in the blood break down the soil. The bones from the slaughter house are used (along with wood) for winter heat of the family home, then ground into bone meal for addition to the acreage. Dave was instrumental in getting university researchers to look into the value of Alaskan fish bones as a nutritional source for soil and he uses fish bone meal on his land.

Pests are not a huge problem in Alaska, the main culprits being root maggots, cutworms and aphids. Dave uses the yellow jugs that Alaskan-grown milk comes in, and puts a sticky organic matter on them; they attract root maggots in their flight to breed and they never leave. He does a great deal of hand removal of cut worms and uses drip irrigation and target weeds to prevent them. Of course, many birds and beneficials are on hand to help.

The vegetables are marketed at the Saturday market, which Dave describes as "a state fair without the rides," that takes place in Anchorage each week. They have 10,000 people come through in a day, and that pretty much takes care of any marketing problems. The market is open from Memorial Day through Labor Day.

Dave learned about organic gardening from his mom while he was growing up in upstate New York. "She was one of the original organic gardeners," says Dave, "I made my first organic garden in the '50s." The one thing he noticed was that the neighbor's vegetables never looked as good as their organically grown vegetables. "It's still true now," he says. "At the farmers' market we get the most customers because our vegetables just look so much better."

It may be that most new farmer-entrepreneurs wearing the organic label simply market this way, or set up farm front "stores" or stands, much like the cheese producers mentioned previously.

The Coleman Ranch, headquartered at Denver, Colorado probably comes closer to qualifying as a structured business in terms of the parameters set out in this *Guide,* and most of the other organic farm enterprises fall somewhere in between. In 1875, before Colorado was a state, Mel Coleman's great-grandfather left Altoona, Pennsylvania to set up the Coleman Ranch in Colorado. Mel Coleman's grandchildren are now the sixth generation Colemans on that ranch. They work more than 250,000 acres of high country raising beef cattle, all organically. When the operation went organic, the ranch employed ten ranch hands. Using a business plan, the ranch has expanded into the multiplier sector in a big way, while calling on some 50 ranches to help supply the natural and organic market. Another 1,000 growers stand ready in the wings to supply animals produced under exacting specifications for the emerging "wholesome" trade.

The Coleman enterprise raises 5,000 head of beef cattle — organically. When getting started in 1979, "no one wanted the product," says Mel. They raise their own herd of organically-produced animals, plus contract with 50 other ranchers to produce meat for the Coleman Natural Meat Company, which employs about 110 people. Additionally, 1,000 ranchers have signed agreements to raise beef under strict Coleman guidelines and monitoring systems, and they are brought in to the business as expansion continues.

The Coleman cattle are raised by grazing. They receive no antibiotics or growth hormones from the time they are born and eat native grasses, with hay put up for winter feeding. The affiliate ranchers agree to use no antibiotics or growth hormones and feed only feeds that have tested free of residues. The entire system is monitored by the Colemans, with farmers and veterinarians signing off on approved herds.

The organic animals are slaughtered in a custom, OCIA-approved slaughterhouse. The meat is vacuum packaged at the Coleman's operation in Denver under USDA inspection and trucked to market as soon as it is packed. They are now selling to some conventional grocers as well as natural and whole food markets. The organic end only accounts for about one percent of the business, the rest is natural.

Mel Coleman started with some fundamental concerns and beliefs. "Using grass sustainably was important — 65 percent of the land is grass and if we use it sustainably it will be a source of renewable energy forever." Another concern was antibiotic use. "We were finding that the antibiotics were less and less effective on the cattle, and we noticed with our own children that they were becoming resistant," says Mel. "We never believed in using those chemicals. And I think the use of growth hormones is sickening. It's wrong to change the fundamental structure of these animals."

But as to the structure of meat farming and processing, the Colemans hope to "change the whole industry." According to their beliefs, "The human and environmental costs are too high with a non-sustainable system. We want to see a more sustainable system in place."

Other marketing systems fall somewhere in between the two immediately mentioned above.

Jean Mills and Carol Eichelberger of Tuscaloosa CSA Farm in Coker, Alabama, sell their several acres of produce CSA-style, with customers picking up their own produce, either individually or as teams, through the seasons. Blueberries are on a pick-yourself basis. These procedures allow them to save time and consumers to save money. Their satisfied customers know they are particicpating in the farming project.

Following California organic standards, Jean and Carol grow four acres of vegetables and a half acre of blueberries by an eight-acre pond on their 30-acre farm. They grow about 35 different vegetables in three distinct growing seasons — spring, summer and fall. January begins the greenhouse seeding, and the first week of April finds them distributing the first of their produce to their CSA customers who each pay premium prices for 32 weeks of fresh, organic produce. Their growing year ends the week before Thanksgiving, but CSA members still come to pick after that time.

Jean says everything is grown in a living mulch of white Dutch clover. The garden is in 100-foot blocks, three-feet wide with two-foot paths in between the blocks. The beds are fertilized with the green manure from the clover and the paths are left alone to grow clover walkways. As part of a SARE organic farming research project, they have been mowing the walkways and composting the clover clippings as the sole nitrogen source in an effort to eliminate off-farm input. Weeds are a problem at the bed edges until the plants grow tall enough to shade out undesired plants. There are ample beneficial insects, and Jean has noticed many more each year since they started.

Their distribution setup is unique. Their CSA members are divided into approximately seven-member geographic groups. Each group sends one person to pick up a harvest for the whole group. This means Jean and Carol don't deliver, and the members only have to pick up produce about four times a year. In addition, they have three CSA members come at 8 a.m. on harvest days to assist with the washing and packaging of the produce and bundling it for the groups. Jean says this allows them to save time and the consumer to save money. It also allows Jean and Carol concentrated time to talk with members about the politics of agriculture and the garden itself. This way "the CSA members know absolutely for sure that they are participating in something significant; it's a good time for them to learn the realities of farming," says Jean.

The CSA Farm has many of the earmarks of a club, as do all "Friends of the Farm" operations. The clientele remains stable month to month and year to year, often taking on the aura of a social organization, sometimes with dues, sometimes not. Some strive to have product every month of the year so that cash flow is stable. Activities are generally diversified, so that berries can supply the income one month, special fowl another, with picnic facilities, fee fishing and a range of products filling in the weeks and months. Many such farms have personal computers and FAX machines for regular communication with customers on special days such as anniversaries, birthdays and holidays.

Gordon and Susan Watkins, Riverdale Gardens, Panthenon, Arkansas simply market their blueberries through the Ozark Organic Growers Association. Certified by OCIA, they sell frozen berries and on-farm through a pick-your-own operation.

Tucked away in the northwest corner of Arkansas, 30 miles south of Harrison, Gordon and Susan have been organic farmers since the '70s when they began with the usual truck farm vegetables. In fact, they were founding members of the Ozark Organic Growers Association. Being in a remote area of the Ozarks, however, was a substantial obstacle to profitability. After a two-year period of researching crops, they decided to focus on blueberries.

They began with one acre of the crop, which has few pest or disease problems. They are up to five acres of blueberries and the farm is thriving, despite being discouraged by Extension agents all the way. "They kept telling me to use fumigants and sterilants, not organic matter," Gordon Watkins says. "Without bragging, our plants are some of the most vigorous and healthy around." Growing techniques were developed mostly by trial and error, and by visiting other growers.

The real mark of success, however, is seen in the organic matter of the soil. Originally less than one percent, they are now able to maintain levels of six to seven percent. "One of the biggest advantages of our system is the breathing room it gives us," Watkins says. "In bad years when cash-flow is tight, we've cut back on the next year's fertilization. We've skipped an entire year's fertilization and haven't noticed an effect." They do, however, continually add organic matter in the form of sawdust.

They market primarily on quality. Berries aren't picked until five to seven days after turning blue; it is then that they are truly plump and sweet. With on-farm cooling, all berries are chilled within two hours of picking. "I used to be naive and thought the organic marketplace was more fair," he says. "You can't slide by on the basis of certification alone."

Bill and Joyce Whipple of Golden River Farm, Fairbanks, Alaska grow seed potatoes and market them mail order, having assembled a roster of customers by advertising in trade journals. Blue potatoes? Red potatoes? Who would have thought that in Alaska someone is experimenting with seed potatoes? Bill and Joyce are trying to develop disease-free heirloom tubers, about 30 varieties, on their 30 acres. Among the varieties they grow are sweets or peanuts, bintjes, finns, and some exotic ancient Peruvian and Indian varieties. They have been farming since 1985 and have been organic since 1991.

They use either a three- or five-year rotation and green manures. They cultivate and plow down grasses which are timothy or blue grass, buckwheat or sometimes oats. Their only additive is Alaskan white cod bonemeal which provides six percent nitrogen, 20 percent calcium, 10 percent phosphorus and one percent potassium. Their main pest problem is with grasshoppers, and they sometimes, but not often, use flaming for pest and weed control.

LIFE'S CHOICE

Jeff Poppen, Long Hungry Creek Farm, Red Boiling Springs, Tennessee, is a farmer who farms on his own terms and is finding the success needed to expand his operation as well as spare time to play the music he loves. His biodynamic farm practices the diversity that biodynamics preaches. On about 200 acres he grows garlic, potatoes, sweet potatoes, buttermilk squash, watermelons, sweet corn, and a variety of vegetables as well as many minor crops such as onions, tomatoes and peppers. He primarily markets both directly to consumers and through health food stoes.

The story goes that his math professor father offered each of his children the opportunity to either attend college or to have their own farm. Jeff chose the farm and, according to friends, got the best side of that deal. Now, incredibly educated, proficient and accomplished, he is expanding his farm, buying more and more land as it becomes available. Located on beautiful terrain, he has a large creek that runs through his farm.

He also runs a nursery operation, selling apple trees with strong, vibrant, full root systems seldom seen from commercial suppliers. He markets these through a catalog. He also raises beef cattle naturally, although he himself is a vegetarian.

Living off the grid, he keeps his expenses at a minimum — no phone and low taxes as much of his land in undeveloped — and he grows his own food.

He makes many of his own biodynamic preps. And somehow he finds time to pen a regular column for his local newspaper, as well.

They sell their product through advertising in vegetable journals, calling organic farmers, and word of mouth with their seed potatoes bringing a much higher price than conventional growers command.

Bill says that growing potatoes through "conventional farming caused too many problems and had a poor bottomline quality-wise, like hollow-heart and growth cracks." In addition to their resistance to defects, organic potatoes store better. "I don't have to use sprout inhibitors," says Bill. But according to the Whipples the best test is to eat them, "eating quality is a whole lot better."

Large or small, those who pursue bio-correct farming seem to have one objective in mind, recasting the existing order of food production and selling.

The Coleman's hope to change the whole industry of red meat production. They hope to do away with the stinking pens that scar the high plains. The human and environmental costs are too high with the prevailing non-sustainable systems.

The smallest garden operations, and eco-farms sized up to and including mega, all share in this objective.

Smart management — the Voisin pasture system at Frasier Farms, Woodrow, Colorado, for instance, and least-cost producers coast to coast benchmark the eco-farming way.

Trying to be a least-cost producer and be kind to the environment is a tough challenge, but it is one that Frasier Farms is accomplishing. Making use of Holistic Resource Management methods, this over-28,000-acre ranch has some 3,000 yearlings summering on 120 paddocks of 250-350 acres each.

Through increasing the herd numbers to four herds of 600 to 1,100 head per herd, they were able to gain more control of grazing time. Also, the higher stock density has a beneficial affect on the ground, when given adequate recovery time.

The benefits are many. "A short-term benefit, from a management point of view, is that you can see all of the cattle in 30 minutes," Frasier says. "Long-term it means more to the land with better health and diversity in the forage population." He also sees healthier water and energy cycles. The short-term resource is the cattle. The long-term resource is the land.

The grazing pattern, or flow, is planned every year to be different from the previous year, and the ranch's layout was designed to be flexible enough to adapt to it. Grazing periods are kept short — two to three days maximum — allowing 30 different paddocks per herd. "If you stay even one-half to one day too long it stresses the herd and runs the risk of damaging the land," Frasier says.

Some areas of the ranch are improving rapidly. "We don't know how productive they will become because they get better and better each year," he says. In other areas the response has been slower.

In keeping with proven Holistic Resource Management methods, long-term monitoring of the land is conducted using annual photos as well as random readings. After a number of years, definite trends become apparent. While some trends follow the weather, most are linked to grazing management. All of the factors, however, are very fluid.

Mark Frasier also sits on the review panel for sustainable agriculture grants.

Tom Seibel has been farming since 1971. He and his wife, Lety grow 30 varieties of gourmet dried beans, specialty grains, and seed on 50 acres of irrigated ground near Anton Chico, New Mexico. Their acreage is a mixture of organic and conventionally tilled ground, furrow irrigated by a community-governed acequia system of canals using water from the Pecos River. The Seibels are brokers for the Seeds of Change seed company and work with growers in Mexico to produce blue and red seed corn. Their farm produces some vegetables, snap bean and corn seed, but their main crop is dried gourmet beans.

They are continually experimenting with different types of beans because each variety has its own peculiarities and cultivation needs which makes the business "somewhat management intensive" according to Tom. The Seibel's look to yield as the deciding factor in which varieties are kept and which are phased out. Yields range from a low of 1,000 pounds per acre to a high of 3,000 pounds per acre. On average, the yield is generally around 1,800 pounds.

After harvest, the beans are sorted. Because there wasn't a local seed company equipped to individually sort and clean the large number of varieties the Seibels grow, they invested in seed cleaning equipment to do it themselves. The seeds are run through an air cleaner, a de-stoner and a gravity separator — a three-stage process. Once cleaned and hand-sorted, the beans are polished and bagged either in 25 or 50-pound bags. Seeds are only air-cleaned, but the beans are polished for the gourmet market where the customer has high expectations regarding product appearance. Tom says, "Prices are good in this kind of niche market, if you find the right contract buyer." But he also says that costs for just polishing and sorting a crop can easily run 40-50 cents per pound.

All these growers compute their cost-in-production to a fine degree. Yet many others allow the tradition of a low supply price to govern retail sales, often taking price cuts — because of competitive loss leaders — that are not only debilitating, but ruin one as well.

Case reports can yield principles, but more often tested principles account for good case reports.

The universities and USDA pretend not to understand parity pricing. As a consequence basic storable commodities are forever at the mercy of low cost producers elsewhere in the world.

Eco-farmers who have given up on that end of agriculture are quite aware of the fact that the world expects the low supply price idea to prevail. It is this concept that has still to be erased. Indeed, many bio-correct farmers have tried to do this, almost always striking their prices pragmatically with little or no attention to the principles of markup maintenance. Here, then, is how the other half lives.

For a moment set aside the connection between farm production and the sale of organic produce at the tailgate or farm store. Ask yourself, what is the anatomy of the markup mechanism? Even without the clear-cut division between primary production and sales at retail, the farmer-entrepreneur is obligated to understand the economics of price cutting and through the weight of his knowledge, believing the concept of his own price maintenance structure. Farmer-entrepreneurs who look to schemes used by mass merchandisers may think they must follow the leader regardless of the demands of the production — sales sequence available to organiculture. Many forget that volume x turnover x small margins = disappointing results. In their eagerness to secure a large volume of business, they forget some of the fundamentals of sound merchandising, whatever the type. Often they will argue and satisfy themselves, and sometimes their listeners, with theoretical calculations based on the assumption that increased volume will mean quicker product turnover and enable them to operate on a smaller gross margin. While these theories appear reasonable, close evaluation of the hundreds of case reports I've seen proves conclusively that they do not work out in practice. Those who have used this mistaken theory in other businesses to their sorrow did not go into their calculations deeply enough to fully understand how much increased business must be secured to offset the loss sustained by cutting the price. If cutting the price would create a new or additional field for the product, there might be some justification for such actions, but unfortunately this is seldom, if ever, true. As a consequence it is not only an unprofitable procedure to the retailer, but is usually ruinous to a trade or industry. Many otherwise shrewd businessmen forget their sixth grade arithmetic.

Here are a few examples that prove arithmetic is the same today as it was when we were in school.

Let's say a farmer-entrepreneur realizes that he must make, say, 25 percent gross margin on sales, therefore he adds $33\frac{1}{3}$ percent to his costs in establishing his selling price. While we're at it, let's bifurcate the farm operation in its production scope from the newly assumed middleman function. Economically, if not institutionally, the farmer sells his production to himself for the purpose of retailing, therefore the cost to the merchandising arm can be established using accepted accounting principles. Farmers are not likely to do this as a continuing bookkeeping device, but for the purposes of comprehending the anatomy of price-making and markup, the following drill is worthwhile.

Using the above formula, if the selling price is $100, cost of goods $75, gross margin equals $25. If, under the pressure of a buyer's market, the entrepreneur weakens, even though he knows a 25 percent gross margin is necessary to absorb administrative and selling expenses, he abandons his better judgment by thinking added volume and faster turnover will compensate for say, a price cut of five percent and he secures the business, the picture then appears as follows;

Sales Price	$95.00
Cost of Produce Sold	$20.00
Gross Margin	$20.00

The cost of the produce sold remains the same, and the cost of doing business has not been reduced, but five dollars of gross margin has been sacrificed, and the only way to recover this is through increased volume.

What happens when the price is cut? To regain the five dollars gross margin sacrificed on the original sale, 25 percent additional business must be obtained, which in this particular case amounts to $23.75. How many produce stands? Do operators realize that when they cut a price five percent, that it is necessary to obtain a 25 percent increase in volume to offset that newfound cost? Is it possible to obtain this 25 percent increase in the sales mechanism this year? In most cases, experience has indicated that the market does not change that rapidly, and that therefore this is impossible. Assuming, however, that there is such a possibility, it means that 25 percent more produce must be handled in and out of the sales facility. Can this be done without affecting present costs?

What happens when special cuts are made? Suppose that when the farmer-entrepreneur endeavors to get added volume, he finds competition keener, or customers a bit lackadaisical in coming around, regardless of price? So following this price-cutting idea to its final conclusion, the entrepreneur cuts not five percent, but 10 percent from the original price in order to secure the business. The sale would then appear as follows:

Sales Price	$90.00
Cost of Produce Sold	$75.00
Gross Margin	$15.00

If the farmer-merchant who yields to a 10 percent cut desires to recoup his gross margin on the basis of larger volume, it will then be necessary for him to obtain $60 additional business or approximately $66\frac{2}{3}$ percent of this on lower sales price.

What does a 15 percent cut mean? I recently had a very heated discussion with a lumber retailer who proposed to take a 15 percent cut in order to secure a HUD order on which, incidentally, he had nothing to gain except the gross margin on that particular sale. During the discussion it soon developed that the man did not realize that to secure the same number of dollars of gross margin, on a 15 percent reduction, it would be necessary for him to increase his sales 150 percent. Needless to say, the proposed 15 percent reduction was not offered. If it had been offered, the sale would have appeared as follows:

Sales Price	$85.00
Cost of Produce Sold	$75.00
Gross Margin	$10.00

The following simple arithmetic was sufficient persuasion.

$85.00 x 2.5 = $212.50
or the new sales volume;
$75.00 x 2.5 = $187.50
cost of sales

This all equals $25 gross margin. These figures clearly illustrate how much peril there is in the big volume, quick turnover idea, and how much damage is done when price cutting becomes the vogue. In a farm-to-market operation it would be ruinous.

Before the selling price is reduced to stimulate business, it should be determined how much the volume will have to be increased in order to make the same margin, in dollars. Consider a 33⅓ percent markup on cost, or a 25 percent on sales, which was the basis used for this example. A five percent cut means 25 percent more volume required,

10 percent means 66⅔ percent more volume required,
12½ percent means 100 percent more volume required,
15 percent means 150 percent more volume required.

This should be a lesson for farmer-entrepreneurs who are anxious to get volume by way of the price-curring route. The question of operating cost has not been considered in this discussion because it must be obvious to everyone that any material increase in volume must have a consequent effect on handling expenses, and while the so-called overhead may not be proportionately affected, nevertheless the selling and administrative expenses will increase significantly.

Does price cutting increase profits? The chart reproduced here illustrates the amount of business that must be obtained to achieve the same gross margin if the price of any commodity is decreased by 3.5 percent, 7.5 percent, 10 percent, etc. It reveals the almost impossible task a price cutter sets for himself. If you anticipate cutting your price to increase sales volume, please note; the percentage of sales increase required to stay even more than make up a dramatic chart. These figures deserve to be com-

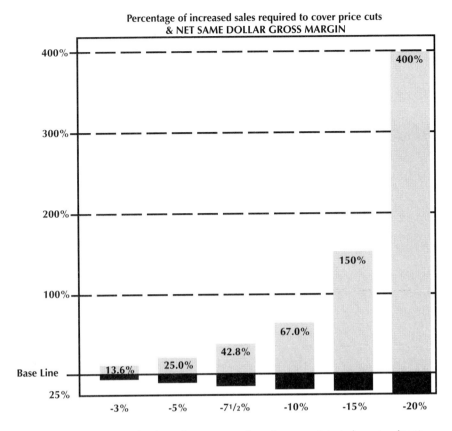

Percentage of increased sales required to cover price cuts
& NET SAME DOLLAR GROSS MARGIN

NOTE: The above figures are predicated on an anticipated margin of 25%.

mitted to memory or to be cut from this book and pasted into each hat, or at least posted near the cash drawer where sales are made.

This entire chapter should be read and re-read and cemented into place through daily application in the selling end of the farm enterprise. For on these data rest the chances of business success or failure. The business you save when you refuse to cut prices may be your own.

Arithmetic plays no favorites, whether the sale is made over the counter, via CSA pick-up, private treaty, subscription, farm club, a friend-of-the-farm club, or pre-contract in Harvard specification buying style, it is the construction of price that governs the bottom line. The *pro forma* package called the business plan, has to take an entrepreneur's notice of all the above as our journey to the bottom line continues in Chapter 13.

According to Lee Fryer in *The American Farmer*, there were six million family farmers in the United States at the end of World War II. Most of them are gone, having ignored the lessons contained in this chapter. USDA figure wranglers tell us there are only 150,000 viable commercial farmers — all of them relief clients — because they forgot, if they ever knew, the simple precepts of marketing, discount, volume, the political right to parity and the anatomy of the business equation.

CHAPTER 13

Management Quotient

Some years ago, while handling an editorial pencil for *Veterinary Medicine* and serving as a consultant for certain retail operations, I published a manual that, up front, posed a number of questions the prospective retailer and/or doctor was required to answer *(see page 122)*.

This test provides a theoretical drawing line between planning a business and actually opening the doors, so to speak. The lessons learned so far have now to be put to use in the real world. Assumptions must now be turned into realities.

Two distinct functions mark the difference between the abstract plan and the firing line, namely buying and selling. In an economic sense, the farmer-entrepreneur buys from himself. He sells to cash-paying customers. Coordination of the two in a manner best calculated to yield a profit at both ends and build goodwill may, in a measure, be regarded as a third function — merchandise control. The performance of the buying, selling and merchandise control function is often called merchandising, and this to most farmers is a new concept. Managing a sales arm for the eco-farm cannot be summed up so simply. There are many ramifications. Therefore this *Guide* will now mix in operating notes with a few projections success and growth would find interesting.

Suffice it to say that in spite of normal business cycles, there is great opportunity awaiting the innovator.

I have already discussed the role of management in determining how much capital must be represented by in-process inventory and fixtures, a correct ratio for rent, salaries demanded, the character of a margin, expenses, net profit, etc. All add up to being the focal point of any business — how to obtain the best possible return for every dollar invested.

MANAGEMENT QUOTIENT

	Check One		Time for Action
	Yes	No	
Do your business records show the profit or loss of each phase of your operation to the people responsible for its supervision as well as to yourself?			
Do you receive a periodic report of cash accounts receivable and accounts payable balances?			Right Now
Do you use your outside accountant for advice and guidance?			
Does your profit and loss statement give you quick and accurate comparisons with last year, and do you receive it by the 10th of the month?			
If there is no profit within a given month are you able to determine why?			
Do you know what markup you need to obtain the desired net profit — in other words, do you know your true overhead?			
Do you have an expense budget for each month?			
Has your overhead, as a percentage of sales, increased within the last year?			
Do you know if your expenses are in line?			
Has your volume of business per employee increased over the last year?			
Do you get out in the field and shop often enough to see what is happening?			Right Now
Have you checked your competitors' methods of doing business recently?			
Do you belong to a trade association in which you can meet competition and discuss job costs on a friendly basis?			
Have you set aside sufficient funds for your salary in case of operating losses next year?			Right Now
Do you have a cash budget for the next 12 months to show you when you may need money?			
Have you met with your banker within the last 12 months?			
Do you budget capital expenditures a year in advance? And do you have a cash reserve set up to replace equipment as it wears out?			

In developing a plan for the farm enterprise, great stress was placed on dovetailing assumptions with resources and reasonable expectations. Now is the time to juxtapose the findings next to census data assembled by National Cash Register Company. Of 5,000 business firms that prospered or died over 80 years, almost one-third lasted only in the neighborhood of one year. Those that survived the first full year found their life expectancy considerably brightened. Only 15 percent failed during their second year; nine percent in the third year, and so on. I have found no meaningful records detailing the birth survival or death of the type of farmer-entrepreneurs envisioned here. But the record now being created by farmers — one at a time — is being expressed in the general expansion of the organic movement.

A review of the foregoing chapters will remind us that there are discernable causes of failure:

1. Insufficient capital.
2. Over optimism.
3. A lack of sufficient business experience, enterprise and ability. Business depressions are not the chief cause of failure, although they will always furnish a plausible alibi.
4. Borrowing too much. An analysis of farm enterprises that fail suggest a high correlation between life span and capital invested by the owner.

Again, here are data calculated by National Cash Register Company covering a long time span.

Cause of Failure	Percent Total
Incompetence	34.5
Inexperience	5.2
Lack of Capital	34.9
Unwise Credit	1.4
Neglect	1.1
Speculation	.3
Fraud	3.6
Miscellaneous	.5
Total	81.5

There are failures that are not the fault of the farmer or other entrepreneur.

Cause	Percent of Failure
Failure of Other	1.3
Competition	2.4
Specific Conditions	14.8
Total	18.5

How about profits? How much can the farmer-entrepreneur expect as a return on his investment, time, energy and resources? Joel Salatin has explained how on-farm activity translates into profits greater than anything available in the "What'll You Give Me?" market. The farmer who wants to recover double the industrial wage for his efforts simply has to recover for the farm many of the functions previously brokered out, but this recovery has to be linked to a sales program.

Without becoming a full-time bookkeeper or cost accountant, the farmer-entrepreneur will have a hard time answering the question of profits. The differences in the ways which entrepreneurs compute their salaries is one of the problems. Entry onto the books of a reasonable figure for owner compensation is a prime requirement. Too many farmers live off their inventory and fail to appreciate the difference between actual profit and the amount that enters the till.

These cautions may seem superfluous in light of the plan and the explanations offered for the think tank phase of business start-up. But if this gentle reminder prevents a rude awakening when the farmer-entrepreneur realizes he has been operating at a loss, then this intellectual carbon copy of a lesson learned will have been worthwhile.

The question that now comes to mind is obvious. How much beyond the farm operation should be earmarked for the sales end of the enterprise? The plan has its answers, of course. But are there any valid codicils? Probably not without getting specific, but one way for a last minute dust-off is to compute operating expenses as a percentage of income. Here we include wages, including wages of the owner, rent (if any), supplies such as packaging, heat, light, power, taxes, insurance, interest, repairs, etc. These are usually lumped together as overhead. The ratio of turnover is not as important a consideration for the vegetable or fruit grower, especially if the product is expected to be sold at harvest. Storable commodities involve special considerations. On balance, the turnover for the farmer-entrepreneur is good. The furrier or even the furniture outlet, as examples, feature merchandise that in the main is slow-moving and high priced. On the other hand, the sales end of the farm enterprise requires a relatively low investment. If the investment is too small, the profits will follow suit.

Pundits in government and colleges will tell you that a capitalization yardstick of 2.5 to one is sufficient for most types of retail enterprise. According to the time-honored rational, for every $20,000 in annual sales, $8,000 capitalization is required. Experience indicates that this ratio does not hold. It does not hold because the minimum for a store that buys its inventory is not the same as a farm operation that bifurcates production of sales inventory and tailgate sales, merely calculating the division mentally. Many wish-book readers have sunk life's savings into a farm enterprise relying on schoolmen to do their arithmetic.

In the final analysis, success or failure is largely up to the farmer-entrepreneur. If he tries to run a $100,000 sales per annum business on $5,000 capitalization and keeps on taking money from the business for unnecessary purposes, or gets too fancy with scales or computers, he may not get into serious difficulty if the sun shines all the time, but the slightest mishap will send the operation into bankruptcy.

First, last and always, it is important to realize that hasty decisions are almost always ill advised.

Customer building

Customer building is nothing more than old-fashioned salesmanship or the art of influencing people. In addition to having a truly unique product line, two important factors are necessary in influencing people to become steady customers: a friendly, concerned and helpful attitude, and an inviting display of farm products. A convenient location is important, but not a must. Some farmer-entrepreneurs tell me that customers liter-

THE CORRECT QUESTIONS

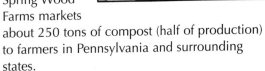

In fertile Lancaster County, Pennsylvania, lies Spring Wood Farms. Comprising 210 rolling acres of cropland, the operation is surrounded by a patchwork of well-kept Amish farms.

Roman L. Stolzfoos, owner-manager, reports that 90 cows are being milked and 80 young stock and steers are being kept. A failure to get results with synthetic chemicals, such as herbicides and insecticides, in the early 1980s, caused him to seek new methods. Intensive management grazing and increasing permanent pasture to 75 percent of the farm have all added to profitability.

Stoltzfoos was also not getting results back when the farm gave poultry drugs. Bypassing the advice of many people who said that it was impossible, Spring Wood marketed its first flock of both "organic" and "drug-free" turkeys in 1989. Currently, 10,000 of their own turkeys per year and 75,000 broiler chickens from another farm are all sold as organic and drug-free.

In 1992, composting by the Siegfried Luebke turner and method was begun. The farm dismantled its "liquid lagoon" manure system in 1994 and began composting all manures from live-stock confinement areas. Presently, Spring Wood Farms markets about 250 tons of compost (half of production) to farmers in Pennsylvania and surrounding states.

Roman Stoltzfoos has been able to perceive the economic benefits in eco-farming or what some call low-input sustainable agriculture. He was able to see that weed, fertility, and productivity problems on the farm hadn't been solved when he paid the custom applicator's bill. Taking poultry off of drugs and changing to more intensive grassland uses with cattle also have demonstrated that, when managed well, being more ecological converts into sound economics. He says that answers don't lie with government, land grant colleges, or county Extension. Solutions must be found by farmers at home on the farm.

Here management principles have decreed that answers await presentation of the correct questions.

ally beat a path to their farms when fresh grain-fed chickens are available, but usually such farms are within an easy drive of population centers. If the farm is in the boonies, a trip over 40 miles may get to be more a journey than a shopping trip. Special advantages will offset location, and that special advantage does not have to be price. Quality is the name of the game. Even journals such as *Bon Appetit* and *Gourmet* are now publishing information on organic foods, the former actually reciting addresses that can be contacted for CSA shipments.

Sales facilities have to be where they have to be, considering resources. Clear paths, clean displays and a look of wholesomeness, all go a long way toward capturing the imagination of the customer — light, especially, should be considered as an invitation. No one likes to poke around in dark places or grope around produce shaded by too much darkness.

Many retailers believe that the first ten seconds determine whether the seller-customer relationship will be a successful one or not.

First impressions are important in all aspects of our everyday lives. They are of even greater importance in building customers. Any farmer-entrepreneur often meets people who simply do not attract his interest. Sometimes it is because they do not smile, because they dress like slobs, or extend a flimsy handclasp. Whatever it is, they are not impressed. The natural reaction is to disregard and avoid such people. Often these unimpressive people become good friends, usually after they are better known. Slowly ripening friendships are good for social life, but for a seller in a business it is quite a different situation. He does not have time for slowly ripening interest. The time with the customer is so short, a first time must be the best.

What can the farmer-entrepreneur do in the first ten seconds to make a good impression?

Let us view the situation from the customer's position. What does he or she see or hear? First, the customer notices the attitude of the farmer or his helper. Second he makes a mental note of the farmer's appearance. Third, he hears the words and tone of voice of the person in charge of the farm, barn stand, or store.

Failure to acknowledge a customer, or visiting problems on the customer is a deal killer. The customer does not patronize the farm enterprise to take on new problems, rather to solve his or her own. Whatever the situation, promptness in recognizing a customer, even with a nod, is more than an icebreaker, it is a half-way step toward closing the sale, and a management mandate.

The attitude should be one of friendliness, helpfulness and concern. An ability to answer questions about nutrition, trade practices and the health equation represented by clean, fresh, wholesome food should be stock in trade for the purveyor of organiculture.

Personal appearance is downgraded these days as being of no importance in making a good impression. Yet it is the appearance and the healthy smile that brings the customer over to the salesman's side. If the feeling that "he or she likes people" is missing, so is the impact available in the first ten seconds.

Ted Whitmer of Glendive, Montana used to tell me of the hostile farmer who totally abandoned preconceived ideas about organic wheat not because of technical jargon, but because of the handclasp. This farmer couldn't stand a fellow who offered a limp hand. He admired a grip, not one to put a man on his knees, yet one strong enough to communicate sincerity. It wasn't the strength, Ted told me, but, "staying on" just a half second longer than is common. "That's what got him to start listening."

Whether the customer is mean tempered, good natured, unmannerly or polite, hurried or curious, stranger or friend, the farmer-entrepreneur should make himself feel friendly to this person. Problem customers will react to a favorable personality. An attitude of service, helpfulness and friendliness will go a long way toward making a good first impression.

It is axiomatic that the prime requisite of selling is product knowledge. Indeed, the reason for being of the eco-farm is the existence of a higher level of knowledge among concerned consumers who are concerned not only about chemicals of organic synthetics in, on and around the food supply, but about the effect of stale and empty foods on human health. Customers of the eco-farm generally have a great deal of knowledge, and they expect the farmer-entrepreneur to have even more.

Most farmers who take back into their operations some of the middleman functions previously brokered out economically, end up with help other than family members. It probably isn't reasonable to expect employees to know everything, but they should know the basic facts about the colorful business of wholesome, toxin-free food production.

Regular customers are the lifeblood of the farm operation, whether it is a CSA, friends-of-the-farm club, or an open treaty operation available to one and all. Few people fail to respond when given special attention such as being addressed by name.

It is not the purpose here to try to turn sellers of organic produce into jerk-leg psychologists. Still, some attention has to be given to the types one is likely to encounter.

Timid. Those customers described as timid are also shy, bashful and often sensitive creatures. Fear and caution are often predominant in their nature. The farmer-entrepreneur should be helpful and reassuring to them when they buy farm production. The timid soul must be given time to adjust to the surroundings, whether these are farm pond, pick-it-yourself patch, whatever. Careful explanation and delicate suggestions make the timid person a steady customer basking in the security of a friendship. Holiday suggestions are of particular value for this type of customer.

Suspicious. The suspicious customer may also be a sentimentalist. He or she is at once distrustful, cautious, unbelieving, doubting and noncooperative. Confidence of the suspicious customer should be gained by being straightforward, cards on the table. Technical knowledge should be a compelling part of the sales presentation. Objections must be met with interest, but not necessarily with submission.

Silent. Customers who rate attention as silent have little to say, sometimes to a point of passive aggression. Their interests are directed inwardly. Introvert, rather than extrovert regarding things or problems. Confidence may be gained by belief in and knowledge of how to cope with steady deterioration of the American food supply. Agreement on minor points may be obtained while the farmer-seller waits for an agreement signal. An honest, straightforward attitude is best.

Irresponsible. Farm operators who invite in the public or friends of the farm — in addition to children — sometimes attract irresponsible adults who often behave like immature children. Swiftness and decisiveness are both necessary in dealing with these people. Sometimes cajoling or flat-

---

A CASE REPORT

When the "Alar thing" hit the Stewart farm in Hood River, Oregon, it nearly devastated the family business. Ron Stewart says, "We felt we had been lied to by the chemical companies. We took a closer look at things and decided that both environmentally and financially speaking, switching to organic was a good move." Since 1988, the Stewart family's 150 acres has been producing a large variety of organic apples and pears, along with cherries and a few peaches. An on-site packing company, Columbia Gorge Organic Fruit, rounds out the farm operation.

When asked about cultivating methods, Ron said "We've been avid *Acres* readers for year – we key off what we learn from the paper." The Stewarts make their own controlled microbial compost on farm using the Luebke method. Cover crops are a blend of buckwheat, vetch, barley and clovers, which are mowed over and incorporated into the soil. They follow the likes of Carey Reams and Dan Skow on soil amendments. They don't worry too much about weeds in the orchard. According to Ron "We hand-hoe young trees and till the orchards annually, mainly to control rodents and keep them from eating the tree bark and roots in winter."

Cover crops hold lots of beneficials and predators and are mowed by alternate rows so there is always a place for beneficials to live. The biggest pest problem they face is codling moths on apples, which they try to control with pheromone releases to interrupt mating. They also use a method of weather monitoring to predict hatches so they can spray with *Bacillus thuringiensis* (Bt) if necessary. There is a lot more scouting and hand removal than there was when they farmed conventionally.

The switch to organic has really brought back the beneficials. The Stewarts now have bird houses and bat houses, mud swallows and tree swallows. "We are seeing more and more as the years go on because they have food here and a good environment without poisons," says Ron.

Once the Stewarts have packed and labeled the fruit, marketing is through an organic broker. They have a nationwide domestic market and some export to Europe. This year they are hoping to expand into the Pacific Rim.

The case report is forever a reminder that how the product is produced neither trumps nor diminishes the side of the merchandising end of the farm enterprise.

tery may be necessary, but a sale is not a given. A wise farmer-entrepreneur does not fall into the trap of catering to such business.

Decisive. These persons are confident, positive, conclusive, overbearing and opinionated. They are often found among professional men and women, and those whose business operations are much larger. Self-styled experts on all phases of eco-agriculture are sometimes found in this group. Caution should be exercised in dealing with them. The customer's opinion on all important points should be obtained and the grammar of the subject should be used carefully.

Deliberate. Characteristically slow and cautious, this person believes he knows the farmer's job. He weighs values and is self-possessed. Again, this behavior pattern is found among certain professional people and very successful businessmen. A great deal of time must be taken in dealing with those who are deliberate. An opportunity for them to think is essential. Patience and caution are necessary. Again, the most technical terminology is essential.

Arguer. Certain customers whose behavior is characterized by inflexibility and obstinance are opinionated, contrary, and generally have foul dispositions. Often they are down-shouters. In dealing with such people it is first, last and always necessary to retain command of the situation. A firm and positive attitude is necessary in relations with the arguer. But the farmer-seller must take pains not to become a down-shouter, or completely destroy the arguer's position.

Impulsive. The impulsive person is impatient and acts on impulse, period. Quick action and a quick sale is to be recommended. Once the sale is closed, don't open it up again with an afterthought recommendation. I've seen such buyers, suddenly confused, walk out without buying anything. Answer the impulse and let it go at that. Most important, get to know your impulsive customer and act accordingly.

Ideal. Most customers are friendly, emotionally balanced and pleasant. They are usually fairly well versed on topics likely to come up, and almost always have fixed and healthy ideas on what the new farmer-entrepreneur is all about.

Indecisive. This type of customer frequently puts off taking action. He is usually affable and ready to listen to any spiel, and more often than not, is not so hesitant if the proper time arrives. Still, his manner is hesitant.

Stubborn. The unfriendly, obstinate, opinionated, over-schooled and half-educated individual may also be called contrary. This kind of person should be allowed to talk since he or she is certain about everything, considerably more than anyone on planet Earth.

The 100 case reports examined in producing the 25th anniversary year issue of *Acres U.S.A.* turned up farmer-entrepreneurs who have encountered all the types mentioned above. Yet these encounters suggest no more than an aside. The focus of attention always becomes established between the ears of the consumer when he or she starts thinking. Those thought impulses turn heretofore managed sheep into high-level thinkers who decide to take their health management into their own hands. That decision, now answered, is a milestone on the route to a better bottom line for the innovative farmer. How well the farmer-entrepreneur answers questions and explains answers determines the management quotient.

CHAPTER 14

Bookkeeping

A t some uncertain moment in time, the farmer-entrepreneur has to face the workaday world of record keeping. The accountant can't and won't handle these chores in most cases simply because they are, indeed, workaday stuff.

Business transactions provide the raw materials, accounting transactions are simply evidence of activity. When business is dull, the number decreases. When business is alive and keen, the number of transactions increase. Without transactions there is no need for financial records. Nor is there a need for the sales apparatus serving the farm. The farmer-entrepreneur who thinks he can function without adequate records will wake up one morning to find that the bankers, the tax collector, the government, all are asking questions about the business.

Some questions are posed from time to time:

1. How much does the enterprise both own and owe?
2. What was the income last month or last year?
3. How much income is derived from various divisions of farm products?
4. What are the overhead expenses?
5. What are the expense items on the income statement?
6. How much are the fixtures worth and what is being allowed for depreciation on expensive scale, whatever.
7. What is the size of the normal inventory of storables?
8. How much does it cost to carry it?

All the questions posed above and many more must be answered in the course of business operation. Almost all decisions have to be made with the aid of records, not estimates, projections or suppositions once the enterprise is under way.

THE SPRAY BROTHERS

The Spray brothers, Rex and Glenn of Mt. Vernon, Ohio, farm nearly all of their 1,400 acres certified organic. They raise soybeans, corn, wheat, spelt and hay. They also raise 75 brood cows and feed out calves. Farming since 1948, they have been organic for more than 25 years.

The management style is similar to their pre-organic days. They use mechanical cultivation and an offset disc. They wait for the ground to

warm instead of doing early rotary hoes on the land.

As for weeds and pests, the Sprays say their fields are as clean or cleaner than their neigh-bors. The best control is a good rotation and resting the land. Rex says, "The more you use chemicals, the more you have to use." Their soil tilth is much better with organics.

They market their organic soybeans at three times the conventional price because of Japanese interest in the product. Spelt is now in high demand because so many people are allergic to wheat flour. They feed their organic corn to their livestock and sell the rest to an organic poultry operation. Their wheat is U.S. marketed and some goes to chicken feed. Their organic beef sells at dressed weight for 30 percent above conventional prices.

When they farmed with chemicals they found they were continually faced with new problems such as stronger weeds and chemical resistant pests. They didn't want the personal risk of handling chemicals any longer. Once they switched over they got a better quality product with reduced costs.

As an opener, there has to be a record of cash receipts and expenditures. These data must be determined with enough detail to satisfy the precepts of prudent management. On the payment side, the farmer-entrepreneur should know the details for disbursements, such as salaries, rent, the minimum required by the bank, the government, and the farmer-entrepreneur's own needs.

The balance sheet and the income statement have been explained in the chapters that dealt with the preparation of a plan. Here it becomes necessary to suggest an audit trail to primary data on which more formal statements are based.

I always favored a daybook of one sort or another. That, of course, is the idea behind the cash register. More often the farmer-entrepreneur simply writes a ticket and the total for the day becomes the receipt's entry. If open invoices are allowed, the ticket can also serve as the invoice. Many accountants want such items posted to a permanent record, a task easily accomplished if computerized record keeping is used. (See Chapter 17, Computer Literacy.) For now, the computer screen may not be a part of a shoestring operation. I have seen a great deal of business done via a cigar box or cash drawer, with tally sheets summarizing data for that legendary daybook. The deposit should hit the daybook total. Co-mingling personal funds, paying expenses out of the drawer, mining the cash receipts for lunch, etc., all contribute to fiction, not bookkeeping.

A very small business may prefer using the charge sales slip as a ledger card, picking up the time sale only when it is actually paid. This procedure keeps gross sales neatly tabulated and in line with bank deposits.

Handling expenses and capital expenditures via checkbook only will save bookkeeping and accounting time, and keeps at arms length those mettlesome time-wasting hunts for misplaced documents. A simple file, A to Z, for backup documents covering checks written is usually sufficient. The basic objective is to furnish the accountant the information needed for statements and tax forms, with an audit trail that adds up all the way.

A good rule of thumb is to design record keeping for the operation. I once served as a city councilman in my hometown. That august body voted to buy a mainframe computer big enough to handle General Motors. Two or three PC units would have been sufficient. With my vote dissenting, the judgment was made to install a monster totally out of tune with the filing requirements for sewer, *ad valorem* levies, etc., and of course the result was one holy mess.

There are simple spread sheets and computer programs for the type of farm enterprise envisioned here. But until the operation grows sufficiently, most of the primary record keeping can be best handled manually.

I have always instructed office help to remember "You can't file a telephone conversation." Often there is a memory failure when an agreement by phone is made. Always make a memo if the matter is of consequence. Or follow-up with a letter recapping the gist of the conversation. If a fax is available, transmit a copy. If not, mail it.

In any case, a balance sheet is merely an elaboration of the equation:

$$\text{Assets} - \text{Liabilities} = \text{Proprietorship}$$

As expressed in the balance sheet, assets are usually listed according to the possibility of their being converted into cash during the year. Such information is useful in making financial decisions. Assets are grouped as current assets and fixed assets. Liabilities are normally listed next, and include such items as accounts payable, notes payable, withholding taxes, social security and taxes. The difference between assets and liabilities is called net worth or proprietorship. As discussed earlier, the balance sheet may be needed for bank transactions. Nevertheless the balance sheet is useful to the farmer-entrepreneur because of the information it contains, always keeping in mind that the farming end of the business almost always exhibits high fixed costs and low variable or out-of-pocket expenses. The net worth of the balance sheet will show in unequivocal terms how much the operation is worth now as opposed to any other period for which records are available. It will show whether a business is stagnant or declining. It will point up the soundness of a financial position. It will quickly tell a farmer-entrepreneur whether he is eating into his capital. An entrepreneur who takes a living expense each week often does not know whether he has earned the money or is merely raiding the till. It has often been said it costs so-and-so much to open the door each day. A farmer-entrepreneur who sells to the public must watch his liquidity and solvency at the same time. If his liabilities exceed his assets, he's certain to taste insolvency. Current assets should be in excess of double liabilities according to accepted accounting principles. Only adequate use of records can help pilot around the sandbars and shallows.

By way of review, we can now put the income or profit and loss statement into perspective. The bottom line is the reason for being in business, the net profit. Recall that in developing this statement, gross profit is developed first, then expenses are deducted to arrive at net profit. In determining the gross profit, it is necessary to develop the cost of goods sold. I have mentioned the bifurcated approach to the farm production-sales sequence. Some parts of this record keeping can be accomplished as memo material or worksheet records without playing into the business of keeping two sets of books, one for the production farm, one for the sales operation. Remember, you're not in business to be a full-time bookkeeper of primary data for an accountant.

The rubrics are simple enough in any case. Cost of goods sold are developed by adding the inventory at the beginning of the period to new additions then subtracting leftover inventory at the end of the period. The difference is the cost of goods sold.

All expenses incurred in the course of business are deducted from gross profit. If a computer is used, the program will usually deliver side-bar information — the percent of the expense factor. Both heavy and small expenses must be watched in terms of these percentages of gross. An expense that creeps away from the norm is to be watched with a great deal of suspicion. It must always be governed by a decision, not a drift.

A new piece of equipment is not an operating expense. Wear and tear — depreciation, in short — is an expense, and deserves to be deducted from gross profit.

After all expenses have been deducted from gross profit, the result is that legendary bottom line that fits into the title of this book.

Withdrawals for the owner should be included among the expenses. This is to insure a knowledge of true costs, but for tax purposes the farmer-entrepreneur defers his whole income, whether classified as wages or as profits. In order to provide this information, a record should be kept of the dollar value of all withdrawals on the part of the owner, and also a record of payments for personal services. The net profit minus withdrawals represents profits available for reinvestment.

Wise decisions are difficult to make without auxiliary records, and no hard and fast rules can be substituted for sound judgment. A business sense seems to be possessed by certain farmer-entrepreneurs who make more right decisions than wrong ones.

Remember, the balance sheet is cumulative. The profit and loss statement deals with the bottom line.

Remember, records can yield results only if the basic data are absolutely accurate. As the computer people say, "gigo," or garbage in, garbage out. Gigo makes sense only if you're in the disposal business. The farmer-entrepreneur is never in the disposal business, as might be the case with the economy of scale farmer; he's in the selling business with one eye on production, the other eye on the bottom line.

One of the best ways to keep a handle on routine sales activity and any breakdown required is the sales spreadsheet. Simple systems can satisfy the basic requirement simply by creating sales tickets or sales tapes generated by the cash drawer. When a computer is available primary documents permit a spread and a balance. I have always like the spreadsheet with a construction style as follows:

Spread Sheet

Time	Date	Gross	Veg	Lamb	Beef	Poultry	Other

The first gross balance balances with the several breakdown totals and a special column or columns can be added to keep track of sales taxes or any other designated piece of information desired.

I used to keep income records this way at *Acres U.S.A.* because the system allowed for a tracking record of the primary document or summary on which each entry was based. Each primary document was filed by the number according to ledger page (or computer page) and line, thus 1.12 became the locator code regarding the amount posted on page 1, line 12.

At the end of each bank deposit period, the total of sales had to balance to gross sales, and/or the several breakdown columns of which sales were comprised. Charge tickets were filed alphabetically and accepted into the sales column only when collected. In other words, they were not considered for daybook tabulation until they had been turned into cash or a check or other instrument. Credit card sales were deposited as cash.

Using this system, receivables remain in limbo during the month. At the end of the accounting period they are added up and presented as open account receivables to the accountant handling the books. When they are collected they become cash sales and are subtracted from the receivables totals. Of course, new receivables are added. The remaining balance is considered income for the income statement, but not for the daybook and deposit control system.

The best way to handle expenses simply is to pay for supplies, inventory, fixed assets, whatever, via check. Each check stub is then coded to the account involved, such codes being pulled from the chart of accounts set up for the operation. If outlays are made in cash, consider this a personal expenditure by the owner or manager. Then pay the owner or manager by check, always filing backup receipts or documents to govern tax for preparation, filing, and year-end income tax return. Any business has to file quarterly IRS and state returns, pay Social Security tabs, enter workmen's compensation reports, sales tax compilations and payments, and at least annually hand off W-2 tickets and 1099 compensation slips to employees and other qualified earners depending on status.

The requirement for the latter suggests a special earnings record replete with withholding data and reference to payments. Often the accounting firm will maintain this brace of records. Ditto for the full codification known as the checks register.

All the above depend on good and timely basic data being kept at the moment of the transaction. Bookkeeping is nothing to cringe at, nor is it something to summon the evil genius called procrastination.

CHAPTER 15

Protecting Your Investment

Without exception, every time a farmer-entrepreneur ventures into the world of commerce heretofore reserved for middle folks or retailers, risks and additional hazards attend the move. There are some aspects of risk peculiar to the farm and sales enterprise. Several are so dangerous that if proper precautions are not taken, risks may wipe out profits and, in some cases, even be responsible for failure. Even the most cautious operation can be robbed, destroyed by fire or sued for damages as a result of a customer falling or sustaining an injury.

Caution is the first line of defense. Whenever you invite the public to the farm, machinery operations should be put on hold, keys removed, unless there are severe restrictions to children and/or grownups gaining access. The farm pond, especially a fish-for-fee operation, poses another danger and commands the farmer-entrepreneur to insure against accidents. Risks of this nature represent a possible loss of capital or interruption of income which could lead to failure.

The farmer-entrepreneur can protect against losses and suit. It is difficult to conceive of a business not having fire insurance. Actually the word *accident* implies a number of possible losses. The hazard of dishonesty may also spell disaster. A figure-juggling bookkeeper, a thieving employee, or a clever thief, any one of these can steal profits unless necessary precautions are taken.

While there are many types of losses, this chapter will concern only those which the most diligent and careful operator may suffer, and against which protection can be interdicted. Major types of losses are:

1. Loss or destruction of physical property.
2. Loss of income.
3. Loss resulting from injury to employees.

4. Loss resulting from injury or damage to the person or property of others.

To more clearly understand how a business person can protect himself against losses, it must first be clearly understood what various terms and types of losses are covered by insurance contracts.

Loss and destruction of physical property can be brought about by fire, storm and wind, explosion, falling trees or aircraft, rot, termites and in a great many other ways. Losses can be incurred through burglary, theft, etc. When such misfortunes befall a business of any type, a part or all of the capital can be lost.

Additionally, loss of income can be brought about by the destruction of property. When damage is done to the building or supplies of a sales property, it is usually necessary to suspend operations until the damaged property can be repaired or replaced. When this occurs, income and profits stop. A clientele it took patient years to build drifts away. If the interruption is a long one, the loss of regular income might well be greater than the amount of actual damage.

Loss resulting from injuries to employees covers a great many contingencies. Most states require the employer to carry workmen's compensation insurance. This usually serves to forestall suit unless negligence can be demonstrated. Many years ago the doctrine was established legally that the employer had a degree of responsibility for accidents to his employees. Thus, the workmen's compensation laws. The employee is entitled to financial compensation for injuries, even if negligence cannot be demonstrated. Compensation is set by law. An employee thus satisfied usually gives up the right to sue.

Losses resulting from injury or damages to the person or property of the public poses many problems for those engaged in expanding the farm operation beyond mere production. Each case must be judged on its own merits. But the courts have given a rather definitive answer to the Biblical question, "Am I my brother's keeper?" by holding that a person is financially responsible should his negligence cause injury. If the farmer-entrepreneur or his employee damages property, the injured person has a right of legal action, and may collect damages at least to the extent of the injuries. For permanent injuries or death, claims sometimes reach staggering amounts. A farmer who is required to pay such damages suffers exactly the same kind of loss of capital he would have suffered had equivalent amounts of property been destroyed by fire, explosion, whatever.

Although the hazards exist, the farmer-entrepreneur can hedge against financial losses. He can protect against risks by transferring risks to a professional bearer, called an insurance company. There are thousands of them, some of them more profitable than the parent company that owns them. They own most of the big buildings in the cities and hold most of the mortgages on farmland and urban homes. They almost never pay willingly; therefore, it is necessary to select the insurance policy company

NATURE BATS LAST

One hundred years ago Leland Eikerman's great-grandfather built the house the Eikerman's live in today near Boubon, Missouri, so when you ask Leland how long he's been farming, he's likely to say, "It seems like forever." The 350-acre farm has 300 acres in organic use. Leland and Carol-Gay grow organic vegetables, cut flowers, dry flowers, bedding plants, hormone/antibiotic-free beef, pork, chicken, and organic eggs and honey.

They sell to a CSA, restaurants, health food stores, the farmers' market and regular farm customers. As much as possible, the crops are sold before they are planted. The Eikerman's idea of good marketing is "to sell as directly as possible to the ultimate consumer."

Leland went organic when he "got tired of working for the chemical companies." He found with chemical farming (he used to farm 3,000 acres conventionally) his yields were getting worse and his weed and pest problems were getting greater. Now he uses bees for pollinators and they give him honey. Lots of birds and beneficial insects are around the farm. He believes that healthy plants and soil attract good insects. Recently he began encouraging bats by putting up bat houses and they do a great job keeping his corn bug free. Sometimes he uses weeds as a green manure crop. Tree trimmers bring him mulch for animal bedding and compost. His yields are good and the Eikerman's are "farming less and liking it more." Leland believes "we have created most farming problems by screwing up the natural balance."

Leland has reported, "We try to make our farm work like the wheel of life with birth, life, death, decay and new birth. Conventional farming is like a cylinder where the resources are buried or washed down the river."

As the state president of the Missouri Organic Organization and a member of the Governor's Agricultural Advisory Committee, as well as a participant in the SARE program, Leland has the opportunity to talk to lots of people. "We all live downstream," he says. "Nature will eventually straighten out what we've done, but will we be here to see it? Remember, nature bats last."

The best insurance has been and remains the correct technology, but greenhouses and facilities can be lost in Missouri storms. Here customer exposure is minimal. Potential loss of economic value is real.

with care and read the clauses for protection with extremely high-level diligence. I have worked for insurance companies in the Meccas of insurance, Baltimore and Chicago, therefore what follows has to be considered "strictly personal."

I do not like policies issued by firms that style themselves as "Group." They seem to obfuscate the exact title of registry in the state, making service of suit more difficult and therefore imposing delay. Delay and bad faith are more common than most carriers like to admit. Faced with such impediments, many people just go away. Legal help is expensive. The prospect of an insurance firm hanging onto money is super-charged by the reality that each dollar earns its component of interest each day that a claim payment is sandbagged or even delayed.

Other things being equal, try to find a casualty carrier that does not employ in-house counsel. If the insurance company has to broker out legal work, the chances of timely settlement are vastly improved. Certainly the laws of insurance favor the claimant, and case rulings have installed some rather exhilarating language into insurance rulings. One in Missouri states quite bluntly that failure to settle in good faith raises the dispute to the level of a tort.

Whenever there is a claim, do not rely on telephone conversations. Remember, the conversation won't file very easily. Cover conversations with your carrier with a letter, and state the claim being made on the enterprise by letter also. If the claim is on behalf of the business — wind or cyclone damage, for instance — document the loss. An annual photo record of the operation is indicated.

Whenever collection does not proceed in a timely manner, don't beg. Just lay the paper on the carrier, first checking with the insurance commission on the registry in the state. Usually this information can be had with a telephone call to the Secretary of State's office.

I realize most farmers cannot be turned into lawyers. Still, filing a suit against an insurance company is simple in the extreme. *Brown's Lawsuit Cookbook,* by Mike Brown, covers general pleading. At the courthouse, the clerk looks and stamps.

DIVERSIFICATION

In the once-rich agricultural lands of central New York state near Memphis, Doug and Penny Bratt farm 250 acres. One man is hired to share the workload of the many farm tasks.

To improve the soil, they have used Fertrell products for 15 years. Fertrell certifies many of its products as organic with the Organic Crop Improvement Association and the Northeast Organic Farmers Association of New York. Doug's crop rotation includes corn for two years, winter cover crops such as spelt, hay for three years, then back to corn. Doug says that balanced soils are the best defense against weeds. In soybean and cornfields, a cultivator and rotary hoe are used.

Milking 55 cows, the farm raises its own heifers as replacement stock. Natural whey products are used with livestock rather than drugs such as antibiotics.

In addition to selling milk and beef, other products are sold, such as corn, soybeans and rye. It has not been necessary for them to get the farm certified organic in order to sell their products, but they are certified. The farm uses 65 percent of its plant crop production.

Doug sees farm practices putting our farms out of business. Farmers have been told that chemicals could ease their workload and increase their profits. Any farmer, just as any householder, can use synthetic chemicals to meet many challenges. In the meantime, on the farm nutrients and soil life deteriorate, lowering yields and farm income. The Bratts are concerned for the next generations and therefore strive to improve soils and life.

Here, again, risk exposure is less than it would be for an operation open to consumer visitors. All systems are natural, and the best insurance is diversification.

This usually gets the attention of the insurance firm. If the claim is less than lawyer costs on a hired-out basis, chances are that settlement will be forthcoming.

If you're on the receiving end of a suit and you're insured, the firm just about has to enter the case. If you're the plaintiff and get greedy, better stop a while and read Jerry Spence's book, *Justice for None*.

To be completely satisfactory, the protection program should be tailored and evaluated with utmost care. Insurance is a technical and highly specialized business, and a complete protection program is an undertaking that requires knowledge, skill and experience. Shopping for the cheapest policy is about the same as buying the cheapest life vest.

If there is one thing American enterprise has achieved, it is the ability to write insurance plans to every conceivable type of risk. Anyone can get insurance for anything from baldness to being hit by a falling meteorite. There seems to be absolutely no risk a person can't insure against. However, it is often up to the insured to make the carrier perform as contracted. The state's insurance commissioner, who will probably find post-government career employment in the insurance industry — is generally worthless or unwilling to help the insured.

The following are insurance packages often of value to the farmer-entrepreneur. A start-up farm enterprise may need some of these, but not all.

Casualty insurance, unlike life, fire, and marine insurance — which are definable by their very names — have definitions that differ by a variety of meanings that may be ascribed to the word casualty because of the wide field of this type of insurance coverage. Quickly and generally stated, it protects the insured against loss from an unfortunate occurrence, which happens without design or without being foreseen. In some instances, such occurrence may cause direct loss to the insured, as for example, a poultry delivery accident. In other cases, it might be when a produce stand is robbed at gunpoint. In these and many other cases, casualty insurance would afford protection for the loss sustained directly or personally. In other cases such an occurrence might cause indirect loss by reason of injury or damage to the property of another person for which the insured might be liable. An example might be an auto accident in which a employee of the insured is injured. The field of casualty insurance in many instances is interrelated with other classes of insurance. For instance, accident and health insurance can be written by both life and casualty companies and burglary insurance can be written by both casualty and surety companies.

Workmen's compensation and liability insurance is required in all 50 states for certain specified employments. There was a minimum required a few years back. Nowadays, it is best to check the agency that deals with the matter in your state. Employers' liability coverage is afforded in the worker's compensation policy to cover the liability of the employer to the employee when the compensation law is not applicable. Premiums are developed via payroll audit.

There are a number of miscellaneous insurance programs which an entrepreneur may buy. Some might be of concern to the farmer turned entrepreneur, others are only of passing interest. Here are a few: burglary and theft insurance covers the insured for loss of, or damage to, property from burglary, theft, larceny, robbery, forgery, fraud, vandalism, malicious mischief, confiscation or wrongful conversion, and against loss or damage to money, securities and other valuable papers resulting from any cause. The trade calls such coverage the "three D's" — dishonesty, disappearance and destruction.

Fortunately, farmer-entrepreneurs do not have the many risks faced by the filling station or liquor store.

If a store results from the farm enterprise evolving to grocery store status, glass insurance might be indicated. Such coverage includes frames and sashes.

Water damage is important in many cases. This covers for loss or damage caused by water resulting from breakage or leakage of sprinklers, plumbing, leaks or roof damage. It includes coverage against accidental damage to pumps, sprinklers and other fire apparatus.

Accident and health insurance has become a business expense even small operators are obliged to consider.

Comprehensive coverage handles dishonesty, disappearance and destruction. This form is a favorite among many businessmen. It protects against loss due to dishonesty of employees, and losses due to the other "D's."

The legalese that attends the full recitation this topic might evoke could put anyone to sleep, and this is not my intention. Withal, it is safe to say that "three D" coverage handles most requirements, and only very special considerations should lead the insured into spending the till empty seeking exotic protection.

I have mentioned fire insurance. It is an absolute must. Admittedly, the fire insurance game makes insurance companies rich, but the risk is probably one no farmer-entrepreneur will want to assume unless the fruit stand isn't worth protecting.

One can find over 100 policies with various clauses for which reason a reputable agent should be enlisted in making a purchase determination. Most fire policies can be written to cover wind, storm, hail, rot, soil motion, police action, strike, smoke damage, a rain of aircraft parts, and motor vehicle crash into the facility. When the likelihood of risk is remote, the premium charge is small.

Since it's easy to become insurance poor, a special study of needs versus expenditures is indicated.

There is one other aspect of insurance that should be of vital interest. More than 90 percent of all business operations are carried on by means of credit extended by lending agencies. One of the first requirements before credit is extended is adequate insurance protection. Insurance facilitates the extension of credit to the farmer-entrepreneur. It also protects credit standing. Just about any entrepreneur will agree that a credit standing is a prized possession.

One last word. Always place insurance purchases with a fully credentialed and licensed agent and company. This is the ounce of prevention only the insured can take. If the choice is good, the claim will be honored. If not, there is the law and the poker game called suit. A go-it-alone plaintiff can always employ counsel if filing suit does not do the job. Such counsel can be invited into a case almost up to the moment the insured steps into court.

Usually insurance claims are settled before that. The high-roller cases you read about in the papers are just that, headlines. If the money gets serious, so do the insurance companies.

Juries may award, but the judges decide. Usually they decide with the insurance company. After all, little people get little justice.

For those who do not wish to discuss this topic so directly, there is always *Brown's Lawsuit Cookbook*. Filing a brief in County Court is child's play. The brief has to be written, of course. Form books at a library can assist. The filing fee has to be paid in cash, a *pro se* litigant being a second class citizen. Needless to say, at least two ultra polite requests stating the claim must background a court's intervention.

Simple casualty claims must be supported by a rationale. If interrogations or depositions are required, answer truthfully and with clarity. Likely a settlement offer will be forthcoming.

I have been involved in several such cases, always successfully. Don't go away mad when a carrier rejects a claim. Help yourself. Your costs are minimal. The insurance carrier has to employ counsel or load down house counsel with something less than high roller stuff.

CHAPTER 16

Intellectual Property

Farmers generally do not trouble themselves about intellectual products. Few products are likely to be new, but there are methods and processes that will be seized in a moment without credit or compensation. Promotional and merchandising ideas, especially written material, is never safe in the open, yet that is exactly where it has to be if it is to serve the bottom line. Packaging, if it is patentable, falls into this category.

Shortly before *Acres U.S.A.* started snailing its way into the mails as a monthly publication, farmer and fish biologist Fletcher Sims, of Canyon, Texas, determined that he would take the composting art out of the backyard and install it near the feedlots that were springing up in the Texas panhandle. He understood the anatomy of breakdown and buildup of compostable materials in terms of billions of unpaid microbial workers, but size reduction of used cow feed as it came out of the lots remained a problem. The Howard rotorator did a fair job breaking down the cement tube blocks of manure, but it wouldn't turn a windrow without recompacting it.

Fletcher developed a turning machine he called the Scarab, so named because the scarab beetle rolls manure and can always be found in residence whenever manure isn't being handled by competing life. Even in the trackless sand of the desert near the Nile River, you'll find the sacred scarab doing its anointed task, rolling camel dung.

Fletcher created a prototype, then brokered the job of making copies to a farmer with a superb machine shop. He filed patents on patentable parts, but forgot to trademark the name he and his family came up with. Before he knew it, the man he'd asked to build new machines for him was in business, improving the machine and selling them under the Scarab name. To continue in business — in addition to making compost and counseling others to do likewise — Sims was forced to create a new name and build a new image all over again.

The point here is that a patent, trade secret, trademark or copyright isn't something commonly considered by the farmer-entrepreneur. As soon as it can be determined that any of the above are eligible for protection, appropriate steps should be taken to invoke their protectionist measures. The several protections are not too complicated, although an attorney might be necessary.

A LAKE HURON FARM

Peter Creguer and family run a 160-acre organic cash crop farm near Minden City, in the "thumb" of Michigan, only nine miles form Lake Huron. He calls it "Twin Pines Organic Farm." Pete grew up on a nearby dairy farm and worked as a herdsman for ten years before buying his farm in 1989.

But rather than stay in the dairy business, Pete has switched over to growing cash crops — although he raises about 20 beef cattle for his family and a few customers. Alarmed by the high cancer rate in his area, one of the highest in the country, he began dropping conventional fertilizers and chemicals. He got help from Midwestern Bio-Ag's Michigan distributor. Finally, Pete decided that he might as well go organic and receive the higher market prices. His farm has been certified OCIA since 1990.

As do many farmers in this area of Michigan, Pete grows edible beans (pinto, kidney and black turtle), edible soybeans, soft wheat, spelt, and vegetables (potatoes and carrots). His typical rotation is: first year, edible beans followed after harvest by winter wheat or spelt; second year, red clover is interseeded in the wheat, which forms a cover crop after wheat harvest; third year, clover is plowed in and soybeans planted, and after harvest a cover crop of rye is planted; fourth year, a summer fallow with rye cover crop, followed by a fall planting of either wheat or another rye cover crop.

Pete has previously used gypsum to add calcium and bring his calcium/magnesium ratio in line. With high soil biological activity, all he needs to do now is add 100 to 200 pounds per acre of organic starter fertilizer. The small amount of manure he has goes on sandy ground.

Pete's farm presents some challenges, however. It has seven different intermingled soil types ranging from muck to sandy loam to clay. But after getting the soil into a good balance, with high biological activity, there is little difference in the performance of each soil. He tilled the farm in 1994, reducing a frequent drainage problem. Close to Lake Huron, the weather is frequently cool and wet. That often leads to beans drowning or getting white mold.

Pete and a neighbor, Jeff Booms, who is also OCIA certified, clean and bag their beans at Jeff's processing facility. Besides belonging to OCIA and the Organic Growers of Michigan, Pete belongs to a 14-member marketing group, the Organic Farmers of Michigan, which he helped found. They set the their own target prices, which has resulted in good profits over the years. Pete's vegetables go to an organic farmers' market in Royal Oak.

Patents come in three styles: plan, design, and utility. The inventor reaches for the utility patent because his brainchild involves a new and useful process, machine, composition of matter, or improvement. This branch of patent law and procedure covers new uses for old devices as well as new combinations of existing and often well known components.

Design patents protect what the name implies — new designs, including appearance.

Plant patents have to do with asexual reproduction of new plant varieties, and probably fall outside the purview of this book. This more recent branch of law has been crafted to accommodate the Supreme Court's ruling on biotechnology. This protection of human engineered life forms has been hotly contested by environmentalists such as Jeremy Rifkin, and can be said to be the nemesis of the organic movement. More recently, attempts have been made to allow genetically engineered microorganisms, plants and products under the rules of the Organic Standards Act, a move that would probably annihilate the very concept of organics.

Utility and design patents, then, are of maximum importance to the farmer-entrepreneur, but only rarely.

No less than three classes of inventions are covered by utility patents. New compounds figure as do new methods of making old compounds. New methods of using either new or old compounds, and combinations can vie for patent protection. Biologicals used by organic producers are a good example. Fertilizers and compounded feeds are protectable.

Mechanical inventions such as Fletcher Sims' flail and/or knife arrangements on a compost turner drum are quite patentable. Most people think of gears and devices when they think of patents. After all, devices are stamped with that telltale number or that patent pending legend. The patent office has buildings full of inventions, all replete with plans and protected. Even computer software is patentable.

The utility patent requires the idea to be new and actually embodied in a "physical form." Steps in a process comply with this requirement. In this case, protection is provided when it is issued, not when the invention is created. The term of this protection runs for seventeen years. During this period the owner has the right and duty to prevent others from using the protected invention. There are no rights before a patent is actually issued and made a matter of record.

The process is not all that complicated. The idea takes form, of course, and after that a patent application has to be completed. Most inventors are terrorized by government paperwork and usually hire an attorney for this work, although this is not necessary. Many inventors complete the applications themselves for routine filing in the United States Patent and Trademark office. The date of filing creates a patent-pending status. By itself, this assures no rights or protection. If, however, the Patents and Trademarks office concludes that the invention deserves patent protection, it issues the necessary patent.

The application calls for a comprehensive explanation of the invention without installing a nuts and bolts catalog in the required plans. Heavy emphasis is placed on comprehensibility. A user should be able to employ the invention without a great deal of experimentation. Narrative and diagrammatic instruction also must be made part of the package.

Here the term "best use" asserts itself. The applicant cannot suggest a secondary part of the invention as a principal use and hide the chief reason for being of the invention for eyewash purposes in order to keep secret the real value of the invention.

A patent has to be filed within a year of any public disclosure, use, sale, or offer to sell. Missing the deadline invalidates any application. Pressures are mounting to eliminate even this single year of grace, in which case an application would have to be filed before any public disclosure takes place. Such a move would put United States patent policy in compliance with policies in other countries.

Whenever a description of the invention is published in a periodical, this constitutes public disclosure. A news article that merely covers who, what, when, where and how, without adequate information is not considered disclosure. In addition to publication, market testing, exhibition or public use by the inventor in effect activates the time period allowed for filing. Use for experimental purposes is an exception. Finally, any sale before filing bars a patent, even if the invention is embodied in some other process or invention so it could not be discovered.

Three requests for information have to be satisfied: a narrative description, a claim or claims, and a drawing or drawings. In the case of chemical compounds, a drawing is not necessary.

Many inventors elect to forgo the protection patents have to offer in order to enforce secrecy. There is some justification for this attitude. The government may grant a patent, but it is up to the holder to detect and enforce infringement. Usually something more than a stern letter is required, that something being a suit at law. The inventor, especially the farmer-entrepreneur inventor, simply can't afford the time to learn legal procedures — the rubrics of pleading, the traverse, interrogatory and final argument in court. In fact, judges are so prejudiced against *pro se* litigants, actual trial procedures almost certainly require a lawyer. Even an hour of useless conversation in a lawyer's office costs a day's wages or more for most people, and the task of teaching an attorney the grammar of the invention is often insurmountable.

This leaves the basic value of the patent in about the same posture as the copyright, a purveyor of moral suasion.

Some few precautions are necessary just the same. If secret processes are used, then non-disclosure agreements are in order. These should be signed by all personnel and others who enter the premises and have a capability of transferring important knowledge into the public domain.

Trade secrets are not likely, and therefore this information is being supplied for educational purposes rather than *Guide* elements because at least a few farmers will find them useful.

After all, most of the real innovations affecting farm progress have come out of farm machine shops. Often a salesman or professor picks up on the development. From there the idea frequently is transported back to the university for testing and validation and — not least — publication. In the process the real inventor is often shoved out. Dan Noorlander is an exception; he invented the California Mastitis Test, and holds the patent, not a common thing. If you read the literature on CMT you will not look in vain if you expect to find Dan Noorlander's name. His timely use of the patent prevented him from being divested of all credit — and royalties.

Due diligence often has been used to stress creation of plans, gathering of information, etc. Now the same caution must be imposed in guarding trade information and secrets. Carelessly allowing casuals to have access to mailing lists, plans, accounting information, bank balances, etc., does not constitute due diligence. Locks and keys and security measures are in order in any business. There are no formal protection procedures, except those that punish theft. Again the remedy is court, not an attractive alternative for a start-up business with its usual cash-flow problems. Inability to prove that precautions were adequate shoots down a civil procedure anyway.

Trade secrets evaporate in two ways. One, an employee bound to confidentiality violates the trust, or two, someone uses illegal means to discover the secrets and appropriates them for use or sale. Most often ex-employees figure in trade secret thefts. It is almost impossible to keep a heads-up employee from learning a great deal about a business in his or her capacity as an employee. This knowledge can be carried off as experience, of course. The line between leaving smarter can be as sharp as a razor's edge. The question arises: Did this employee simply learn on the job? Or did the employee convert information property — company property, the mailing list or a list of accounts, for instance? Frequently the role of the ex-employee surfaces when accounts disappear or go elsewhere. Investigation then reveals the presence of a competition guided by the ex-employee.

One of the requirements for success as a farmer-entrepreneur is the education of the market. To be sure excellent journals, organization and public information programs build and expand the organic market routinely. The farmer-entrepreneur can't simply sit back and harvest the benefits. The consumer has to be directed and refurbished in the opinion that organic production is superior. In the process, original material — both promotional and educational — may be created. Often the enterprise wants the customer to copy articles and informational broadsides. The oldest trick in the world is for the writer to insert the name of the farm or the store, whatever, into the text at least once for the commercial value. Even the competitor can now reprint with abandon, and this often happens without permission.

When, then, is it advisable to copyright material? And how difficult is it to get a copyright?

The last question is easy to answer. You have a copyright for your book, advertisement, manual, catalog, whatever, if you created the work. Included in the inventory of intellectual works covered are photographs, films, slide shows, typed messages and talks. The term *writings* has been so broadly interpreted, it includes almost anything from mind of man not covered elsewhere. Software programs for the computer are merely come-lately entries in the protected roster. Even the stuff in an electronic memory bank is covered by this law.

Unfortunately, the world has produced some dishonest people, and discovery of intellectual theft is as hard to come by as academic freedom in a grant-funded university department.

Some few years ago, I created a set of slides entitled, *The Case for Eco-Agriculture*. The 96 slides and its soundtrack were offered to the organic community. About two dozen sets were sold. Probably four times that many were circulated as pirated copies. Finding the culprit was like nailing jelly to the wall.

As revised, copyright law protects an author and the form of his expression for the lifetime of the author and another fifty years. This rule is modified for works created for artificial persons such as a corporation or a trust, in which case the term of protection is seventy-five years dated from first publication, or 100 years from date of creation, the shortest applicable period being the applicable one. The term *creation* is choice when it comes to copyrights, "the form of expression" being a key factor. A statue of, say, St. Isadore, the plowman, can be copyrighted. So can a dust bowl picture by Dorthea Lange, or the camera work of Ansel Adams. A hammer won't qualify, but a poem entitled *The Hammer* will.

In fact, that slide series styled *The Case for Eco-Agriculture* was not copyrighted because I failed to identify the product with a "©" symbol, or a copyright notice plus date, or the abbreviation *Copr.*, all followed by the date and the name of the owner, thus;

© Copyright (date)
Charles Walters

When I finally wrote a book using the same title, the correct information appeared on the reverse side of the title page. In the case of a statue of St. Isadore, the legend would have to be stamped on the base and be readable.

If even a few copies of a copyrighted work are printed and circulated without the notice, the copyright is gone, no exceptions. Unpublished works — your manuscript, for instance — are hard to be kept secret and are therefore protected under law.

Failure to add the mandatory copyright language does not necessarily extinguish right under a new law, circa 1976. If only a handful of copies have escaped into circulation, a notice can be hand stamped in a published work, and a formal copyright application is filed within five years.

The law is the thing, but not everyone is clear on just what the law is — before March 1989. At that point the United States came into compliance with the Berne Convention. The International Copyright Treaty installed by the Berne Convention required signatory nations to eliminate formalities. This means that if you produced the work, you're copyrighted. Thus you can still file the copyright, and it will strengthen your case in court — that is — if you find out about the infringement and think it worthwhile to pursue the matter.

Statutory damages allowed by law can run up to $500,000 without proof of damage. Here, however, the copyright has to have been filed to make a good case. Filing may be one of the simplest pieces of paperwork ever created by a bureaucrat. Anyone can do it, first asking for the appropriate forms from the Copyright Office, Library of Congress, Washington, D.C 20540-4320.

A fee of ten dollars is required together with two copies of the work. If the work is unpublished, only one copy is required.

The trademark is not copyrighted, it is registered, much like a patent, the meaning of the familiar TM symbol. The key here is that the TM word cannot be descriptive. You can't trademark the word pie to indicate a pie, but a magazine named *Pie*, because it deals with charts created in the form of a pie to express economic divisions would likely find acceptance at the trademark office. Shapes, trees, animals, human beings, and configurations of a variety of shapes and colors rate attention in the trademark lexicon. Businesses that use a special construction style can be protected under trademark statutes, rules and regulations.

Most likely, the farmer-entrepreneur would be interested in the service mark. Blue Cross-Blue Shield designates health insurance and Wendy's designates restaurant services. The mark protects itself by being advertised — and performing. The difference may seem subtle, but it can be explained easily, the trademark must be used on goods, the second in conjunction with a service.

Fraternities and lodges also can have a protected mark — Knights of Columbus, the Elks and Kiwanis certification marks denote quality or a standard, as in the case with organic certification under the auspices of a number of agencies.

Some farmer-entrepreneurs who have entered the distribution end of the food supply business have developed logos to identify the fryers they sell or even the baking potatoes mail-ordered to gourmet customers. These should be protected by trademark registration.

It is not necessary to detain the reader with a discussion of names and ideas that command attention. The turn-of-the last century actress Lotta Crabtree was often told to take on a stage name, that Crabtree had no class. She always replied, "No, this is my family's name, and I'll make it famous." She did. The name used to designate organic production has to be built. There are always imitators. An unprotected trademark is an open invitation for imitation, which confuses the public.

The organic enterprise states its claim on a trademark by being the first to use it in trade channels. It simply belongs to the inventor as long as it is used. In high-level commerce, care is taken to prevent a trademark from becoming generic. If you use the term Styrofoam without a capital letter or a TM symbol, you'll hear from the Dow Chemical Company. The curt but friendly letter will warn that Styrofoam is protected property and cannot be used in a generic way to describe beaded plastic material. Dow Chemical is simply trying to prevent Styrofoam from becoming generic, as has been the case with aspirin, linoleum and dozens of other product names.

Registering an organic trademark requires a search to determine whether the name has been taken. When Jim McHale was seeking a name for Nitromaxx, dozens of terms were considered. Surprisingly, many had been conjured up by other entrepreneurs. Finally it was developed that Nitromaxx hadn't been taken. The search proved fruitful because it prevented a costly error, the cost of printing does not permit such errors if the bottom line is to be protected.

Business counselors say there is no need to register a mark, and they are correct, technically. Still, there are benefits associated with due course registration. States have procedures for registration, but the choice is federal registration, especially if sales are likely to cross state lines. Federal registration is good for all fifty states. There is a requirement that the federally registered mark be used in interstate or foreign trade. Even if cross-border traffic involves only one state, this activates protection in all fifty states.

One other caveat should be considered. Registrations must be renewed periodically, even though continued use invokes common law protection. Federal registration is good for twenty years if filed before November 16, 1989, ten years if filed after that date. There are exceptions, albeit none that affect the organic grower.

As with other legal matters, the old common law is being vacated by statutes designed for that purpose. Nowadays a mark can be registered by application, but use must proceed within six months. Good cause can extend the period, always at the cost of additional hassle. Most important — the mere filing of an application installs rights over others who fail to comply with federal paperwork.

One final word on this subject. Federal law does not permit the sale of a trademark like a crate of oranges or a patent or the copyright of a non-

INVOKING THE LAW

Jim and Megan Gerristen organically farm 100 acres in the Maine north country where potatoes and spruce trees reign. Certified organic by the Maine Organic Farmers and Gardeners' Association (MOFGA), the farm operation engages apprentices mostly referred by that organization.

About 45 acres are cultivated using both tractors and horses. Potatoes are produced and hand picked from seven acres after they are mechanically brought to the surface. Three acres are in vegetables, one and one-half in apples, and four produce grains/clovers. In addition to potatoes, the farm produces many other vegetables, and grains, maple syrup, lambs, strawberries, herbs, forages and pasture. Horses till the vegetable fields. Soil fertility is maintained with animal manures, green manure cover crops, fish scales from coastal fisheries, and crop rotation.

Jim considers marketing to be fully as important as growing. Seed potatoes are sold to a large Maine seed company and through the farm's mail-order catalog. Gourmet table potatoes are sold to the farm's Community Supported Agriculture project and to restaurants as far away as Boston and New York. Vegetables and fruits are supplied to the CSA, which is now in its fourth year and involves more than 30 families. Through mail order, a customer can order onions, cabbages, squash, pumpkins, carrots, beets, beans, grains, garlic, maple syrup and potatoes.

Megan produces a CSA newsletter every other week that contains messages from members, recipes, and crop information. Jim serves on the certification committee of the Organic Crop Improvement Association (OCIA).

Using $6,000 of his savings in 1976, Jim purchased the first 40 acres. There are now seven buildings housing farm operations. Jim attributes their success to hard work, help, learning from other farmers in the region, and steering clear of large debts.

Jim and Megan Gerristen with their son Peter.

intellectual work. It can be sold only with the business it represents.

A license can be granted for use of a trademark, but brokering out a trademark implies the owner will govern the quality and standards of the business or product or service. This requirement cannot be fulfilled by winking an eye or completing a form. It requires inspection and compliance rules that are part of the license contract. Suitable records of tests and other safeguards must be made a matter of record.

The bottom line here is that you have a copyright, but the protection is merely an enabling law that allows you to protect yourself, and to assume the costs. If you think your time can be spent profitably playing lawyer, you can easily assemble basic knowledge by reading *Brown's Lawsuit Cookbook*.

It isn't difficult, but you have to be cut out for it. I have now handled six of my own cases, and brokered out the rest. One of the worst was an infringement case in which a fellow simply reproduced an entire book by camera and copy machine, and sold it at half price. Jerry Barringer handled the case and took a judgment. It was worthless. The fellow was judgment proof, meaning he owned nothing except the clothes on his back and a car not worth the price of the trip it would have taken to seize it. His only comment; "I was trying to help you spread the word."

One case was dismissed on my motion, and the rest had to do with insurance claims. You can sue insurance companies, often successfully, because they will settle if the claim is not too big. "Too big" is measured by lawyer time; if you cost them more than you're asking, they will probably settle because — under Missouri law — if the settlement process is not pursued in earnest, the dispute is raised to the level of a tort.

The farmer-entrepreneur is most likely to be faced by smaller claims. Often these can be settled in small claims court. The clerk will provide instructions, and anyone who is literate can write up the case. If the claim is valid, judgment arises from the proceeding. Like the "Yer honor" in front of the judge, this means little. And the court won't help you collect. If the defendant is covered by insurance, the carrier likely will pay.

Admittedly, these few notes are a "once over lightly" treatment. Laws covering the full range of protection problems are so extensive they fill libraries without even touching international compliances. But for the purposes of this bottom line manual these paragraphs should be sufficient.

Obviously, intellectual property has value — what is that value? Each entrepreneur has to be his or her own judge. For the present, it would be of some value to recite trade practices. There are numbers from which to increase or decrease the negotiated agreement.

For instance, the going rate for a nonexclusive right to use a patent, trade secret or special procedure is five percent. Nonexclusive royalties are 10 percent, 20 percent, even more. The exclusive license is always higher because it allows a virtual monopoly for the object of the license. Such contracts usually call for a performance level. Failure to achieve the target figures cancels the deal.

Always remember, the eco-farm is not a commodity farm. It is a reputation enterprise, and any reputation worth having requires intellectual property, probably starting with brand identification.

CHAPTER 17

Computer Literacy

The only justification I have for writing this chapter is my confession that I am no computer expert. An expert tends to make the subject incomprehensible, a real deficit because many farmer-entrepreneurs are frightened out of their wits by computers in the first place.

I first encountered the modern computer while I was associated with NFO. The machine was a behemoth that filled a fair-sized storeroom. It was always spitting out bushels of punched cards. In order to protect the environment in which this machine did its thing, the place was sealed, air-conditioned and humidity controlled, and generally off-limits.

I next met up with the computer world shortly after I started *Acres U.S.A.* Tandy Corporation had over half of the small computer business, and I figured the company couldn't possibly blow such a lead. I was wrong. Within two years this Radio Shack line was down to about five percent of the business, and the clumsy memory seemed half big enough to handle the traffic. The traffic was largely typesetting and list maintenance and the paper was growing too fast to allow a manual subscriber card system to survive. The Compugraphic was a film typesetter. It cost the price of a Cadillac car even though it contained little more than breath-taking simplicity under its TM blue canopy. I was even able to exchange computer chips and solder into place worn keys — but alas, this computerized film typesetter became as obsolete as any geography book attempting to defend the flat-earth theory. A new development exploded across the business scene, and with it came new languages, nomenclature, acronyms such as DOS and concepts such as integrated circuits and wholly revolutionary manufacturing techniques. In the early days, circuits were painted on, later they were printed. State-of-the-arts changes no longer waited for a new generation to find acceptance. The rollover came each two or three years. The small PC came on-scene while farmers still debated toxic technology. A small disc could handle and store mountains of information with a keyboard not too much different than the one developed for a typewriter.

Computer literacy meant a great deal more in those days than it does now. You had to write your own program if you wanted this machine to alleviate rather than create work. The experts wrote what they called assembler language. Basically they manipulated the ones and zeroes. This made programming very complicated and for most practical purposes kept the innovation out of the hands of the farmer-entrepreneurs. In short, the trade figured out how to make a program that still another program could use. Professional nerds then crafted interpreters usually characterized as first generation languages, second generation languages, and so on.

If this sounds arcane, it is only because knowledge of the above is not necessary in order to make use of the computer in business. Anyone who buys a computer today, and supplies the business with a good program for that business, can be considered computer literate in a few days simply by paying attention, taking instruction from the provider, and consulting the manual when necessary. The process has become that simplified.

Nor is it necessary to enroll at the local community college in order to plug in the computer for valuable assistance in operating a farm enterprise. There are, in fact, excellent programs that fit the needs of the farmer-entrepreneur.

Anyone who consults the Internet (explained later in this chapter) can find several sources for programs. Some firms even permit trial use for a month at no charge. This trade practice allows the user to make certain that the package fits the needs of the farmer-entrepreneur.

For instance, there are so many Internet listings under FARM SOFTWARE that I am not presenting a list here because it would become obsolete even while you are turning the page.

Many firms list the farm shows they will be attending in order to demonstrate their software.

From this writer's chair it seems that the best way to find software is to network with other like-minded farmers to find out what they are using. Most computer users are happy to show interested parties what they are using.

Farming operations are unique nevertheless. Each farm is different in the same way the lay of the land is different. Each unit has its own history, production records, resources, machinery, whatever. No program is entirely satisfactory as written, even though many can be used without changing even one line in the script. Fortunately the art and science of computer management comes to the rescue. Most software is modifiable in that the basic core program does not change. This feature allows the user to add in the parameters that are needed.

A great deal of software is tied into sensors. An example: GPS, the global positioning system. This feature enables active tracking of field positions and conditions. There are even sensors that test for moisture levels. Not all software is that sophisticated, nor does farming require such awesome displays even though the shills for massive computerized farming imply as much.

The best package for the job is the thing. Re-examination of the premises contained in this book is a realistic approach. Although not mentioned earlier, eco-technology invites computer storehouse capabilities and tracking for soil information, input usage and historical acre profiles, some of which emerge directly in the business equation, some not. Some farmer-entrepreneurs pick up on computer literacy quite easily, others might benefit from short-course instruction.

This matter of literacy used to be a significant deficit. Programs were either unavailable or difficult to construct when *Acres U.S.A.* tried to avail itself of this technology. In fact, the first PC sat in the storeroom for eight months before we got it on line. My son Fred and an associate named Garth Bare graduated from the University of Missouri during the time frame involved. The two disappeared into the storeroom for months. When they emerged, they knew computers, especially the Radio Shack IBM compatible.

I had already written the record keeping and operating system described herein. Now surfaced the adaptation job, namely making the computer do what we wanted. This meant invoking the simple algebra required to program each stop down to the last comma and period. Since computers do not like superfluous commas, punctuation was generally left out. Such scripting is no longer necessary. It may be that Ross Perot broke the log jam when he discerned the need for scripting, and concluded that software was a good chunk of business. Today so much good software is available, the exercise of doing from scratch what we did from scratch compares with digging a field when a tillage tool is available as pure blockheadedness.

We needed a business register. Once instructed to do the job, the computer supplied one. We need the systematic accumulation of information for an income statement, balance sheet, cash flow statement, and lesser statements such as receivables and data for accounting records leading to tax returns, and the programmed computer complied. Each of the workers responsible for these tasks was trained by Bare. The items enumerated above are now a part of any good farm software package. In the case of *Acres U.S.A.* this was the typesetting requirement. With a few modifications, this type of software became increasingly available. Basic word processor programs presently do what we had to do the hard way.

The early PC units called for more commands than one might hear from a drill field sergeant. Most of these chores have been swept aside by programs that prompt and/or illustrate. Windows is a case in point. Win-

BOGGY CREEK FARM

Boggy Creek Farm is located at the east edge of Austin, Texas. Larry Butler and Carol Ann Sagle are proprietors of this five-acre plot surrounded by a sprawling city development.

Boggy Creek embodies most of the principles covered in this book with emphasis on communications and marketing. In any month, tapes go out by mail and messages find routine exposure on the Internet and via e-mail. Boggy Creek has a logo and a mascot. All efforts are dovetailed for the purpose of exciting consumers who hit the drive on Wednesdays and Saturdays. The fare is vegetables produced on the home place and on an outback plot kept largely in wilderness. Meats on the sales line are imported from Richard and Peggy Sechrist, an organic meat protein producer at Fredericksburg, Texas.

A "small is beautiful" philosophy underwrites Boggy Creek Farm. It says economy of scale is a poor ticket to farm properly. Conventional advice tells farmers to get big or get out. Most farmers respond by expanding their capitalization and interest payments per acre, downgrad-ing production per acre. In fact economy of scale is a delusion, according to Boggy Creek philosophy. "If you don't want to market, you may as well understand you're working for the other guy," says Larry Butler.

Boggy Creek sells the best produce to customers who keep in touch by computer. The rest enters the retail trade and restaurants, and the farmers' market. The farm's salad mix is usually exhausted by driveway customers. Boggy Creek started selling to grocery stores in 1990. As a consequence the farm has developed a local reputation, one enhanced by romantically imaginative and delightful forays into public relations. Stories on tape recapture the values for consumers.

One additional word. Boggy Creek believes in maintaining its prices. At times when Idaho potatoes are selling for one cent a pound, Butler and Carol Ann get one dollar a pound.

As explained in an earlier chapter, the price cutter is a hazard to the farm.

dows is a graphical user interface. This means it has pictures and illustrations instead of "all text" on the screen. Windows permits use of a mouse to click commands. Thus, without keyboard instructions, programs can be opened quite simply. Windows also allows multi-tasks to be performed. This means multiple programs can be opened at the same time. Suppose the office has a bunch of number crunching to do. Let's say the task is to sort out all customers with an interest in range-fed chickens. The computer has to go through a database assembled over a period of time and process that data. Such as task might tie up the machine an hour, depending on the size of the assembled data. With windows it is possible to open a second program and do, say, word processing while the sort is being made. Or, it may be necessary to compare a spread sheet with a word sequence in process, and going back and forth. In primitive times you had to close down the spread sheet completely and, after waiting for it to load, open up the word processor. Windows allows this shortfall to be sidestepped. Windows, in fact, permits a split of the screen so that two windows can be scrutinized and worked simultaneously. The benefit of being able to view one statement and literally watch it flow into the next month's statement is at once apparent, all without destruction of the earlier statement.

On balance, McIntosh and/or Apple have the simplest programs, even though IBM-compatible seems destined to win out and is considered by many to be state-of-the-arts.

Is the computer necessary in a farm operation? Not necessarily. The world lived very well before the floppy disc or the hard drive was invented. In fact many tasks are best performed manually. A successful business has to set up an audit trail, not only to satisfy government auditors, but also to keep the operation functioning with professional regularity. Those 1099s and W-2s have to go out at the end of the year. The quarterly wage and hour papers have to be filed and sales tax returns cry out for timely completion. In a very small enterprise it is often a moot point whether these "must do" items need to be computerized. A farmer-entrepreneur who writes only a dozen checks should probably forgo the computerized check writing potential and even a spread sheet check register. It is the traffic that prompts the judgment.

In publication work, every transaction has to be trackable down to the piece of butcher paper on which a short note with a check arrives. This is not necessary where there is a cash register and/or a till. Nevertheless, a record of sales has to be made and preferably tied to deposits. Insurance auditors and government gumshoes insist on it. One of the worst practices imaginable is to commingle personal monies with business traffic, or to mix personal expenses with pay-outs belonging to the business. When the wage and hour or income tax people come around, such practices send up a red flag.

Whether the books are kept manually or on a computer, it is probably a good idea to settle for raw data maintenance and leave the construction of final statements and tax returns to a professional accountant. The codes nowadays are too complicated for casual use. Indeed, if the farmer-entrepreneur does not want to spend an inordinate amount time being a bookkeeper, then transfer of basic data to an accountant is indicated. This functionary will need gross sales tied to bank deposits if possible and check stubs for all monies spent coded to the chart of accounts illustrated earlier in this book.

Inventory figures for the end of the accounting period also must be supplied. A tabulation — usually a gross figure — of receivables more or less completes the package. Needless to say, support papers for all checks written must be keyed and kept on file.

A good accountant will harvest the data required for various reports from raw information presented. For instance, if a piece of equipment is purchased, the accountant will set up a depreciation schedule and convert the cost to expense data for you. You can keep your own employment records or let the accountant handle the details as picked up from the coded check stubs. Many small businesses operate quite successfully with only minimal use of a computer. The judgment on whether to use software or bare knuckle record keeping always remains in the businessman's home court.

The accountant uses the computer to speed up and perform the math correctly, making extensions rapid fire rather than tedious work. Even more important, the accountant uses the computer for printing purposes. The saving in not having to type forms or statements is fantastic. The capacity for keeping track of needed business information over a long period of time is possibly the most important feature of any software system.

There is a computer program called Quickbooks, by Intuit, that asks instructions on where an item goes on the income tax. The judgments regarding use of an item are made at the time the books are set up. Transfer of data flow has done much to uncomplicate what may be the most complicated taxing system in history.

The near bottom line being expressed here is that you can use any degree of sophistication you want. You can still do the record chore manually with the assistance of the computer, or you can turn it all over to the computer as the raw material is developed and have the system spit out the product.

Accounting services operate after the fact. By the time the service gets the information, the checks have been written, the debt has been constructed, the equipment has been purchased, and the sale has been made. Sometimes computerized systems start with a purchase order, track the transaction through accounts payable, and even set up signals on when a check has to be cut in order to get a discount. Prompts can be programmed to furnish a "to do" list when the computer is turned on in the morning.

The accounting firm I used said simply, "I never modify a canned program. Tampering with one is really kicking over a bucket of worms." My own staff was never that reluctant. It seems we could modify a program to do everything except cook a ham sandwich. Admittedly the old programs, which used to list a program line by line, made modifications possible. Nowadays, modification has become so complicated, you better ask yourself if you have nerd qualification before tackling the sport.

Any card carrying nerd can tell you all about megabytes, gigibytes, etc., but most of this lingo is superfluous to a farmer-entrepreneur trying to get paid for as much wealth as he produces.

Everyone hears horror stories about a PC being obsolete in two or three years. And yet I see systems that have been in operation for up to 15 years without modification. Most of the "demand" for faster, bigger units with almost main-frame status is a result of hype. This is not to deny the CD ROM and search engine capabilities — both of which must bow to the reasonability of need. The accountant needs encyclopedia capability at his or her fingertips. The same may be a luxury toy and a time consumer for someone who needs to tend the crop.

Computer literacy has taken on an added tier of trials more recently with the development of the Internet. Millions of people are plugged into the Internet at the time of this copyright, and this simple fact requires some attention.

The Internet was started in the 1960s as a defense project. Its purpose was to allow scientists and the military to share material in times of crisis, nuclear war for instance. The idea was to create a decentralized network so that the elimination of one computer did not deliver a fatal blow to the military-university complex.

Internet runs off cables, telephone wires, even fiber optic lines and wireless communication systems. The original setup was by the federal government. In short order the universities more or less took command by managing the nerds. Private companies are now involved. The web is only one part of the Internet. It was developed by the University of Illinois, Champagne-Urbana, where they had a big computer center (the mythical-real birthplace of Hal, the *2001, A Space Odyssey* computer). It was this center that developed the idea of a World-Wide Web run over the Internet. Instead of looking at a directory of files, web enabled presentation of graphic material for location purposes. In short, it permitted a "looksee" without having to download the entire file. The web is a sort of Chinese Wall bulletin board. Anyone who finds interest in a web site can call it up and have a look or download.

The system is simple in the extreme. Suppose you're interested in kenaf. A search engine will call up all references to the weed, its uses, prospects for cloth and paper, whatever. How to grow, sell, use, fabricate — all can be part of the discovered package. Not excluded is marketing information. It was this prospect that prompted former NFO publicity man Thayne Cozart and ex-president Steven Halloran to plug in a web page for hog marketing. National Organization for Raw Materials has a web page, as does *Acres U.S.A.* The *Acres U.S.A.* site is www.acresusa.com. Websites are ephemeral. They come and they go. Even dot com businesses fold, as did over 1,000 in 2001, as an example.

Cozart's comment on the potential of the web for bio-farmers is not without interest. "There's a gigantic market out there which is usually perceived as a monolith. The web enables the farmer to break that monolith down into niche or sub-niche markets. It enables a buyer and a seller with specific needs to get together for a time period or a geographic area. The farmer never has been able to do that. The Internet and the web offer that capability."

AgriOne records reveal thousands of hits each year and many hundreds of producers willing to put together small deals rather than to be chewed up and spit out by the giants. These requests are from all over the world, a cry that in effect says, "We don't want to deal with the big boys if we can possibly work a deal with the little guy."

It may be impossible to trace out the first use of the computer in agriculture. In the early 1970s, *Acres U.S.A.* carried story lines on Computerized Farms that grew potatoes, onions, alfalfa, and other crops along the Snake River in Idaho by C.J. Fenzau, consultant. Basically, nutrient loads, water irrigation and yields, and mathematical extensions of soil audits, were handled via computers linked to a mainframe.

It was not until the IBM PC came on line in 1981 that the computer became a viable tool for the production farm, especially one operating as a farm with entrepreneurship attached. The adaptation of the PC for farm operation has become so phenomenal that many consultants now predict a clean sweep in ten years, with practically no one surviving in farming — especially eco-farming — without making use of this tool. Soil tests, already faxed to clients routinely, can be sent via E-mail.

There was a time when farmers equated computers and the Internet in terms of information. The arrival of the Internet site has expanded the instrument's usefulness into commerce. As with all innovations, this one threatens the existing order, in this case the mass market. As far as the eco-farmer is concerned, there is no mass market. There are only thousands of niche markets. The computer can help identify those niches and enable you to serve them.

Thayne Cozart put it this way: "For the first time in history, you the farmer, stockman, business person, and any network of producers can directly merchandise into these myriad mass market niches on a competitive basis, locally, regionally, statewide, nationwide or worldwide."

Cozart illustrated how to plan that merchandising work, and how to work the plan. An abstract in depth follows.

In fact the mass market is little more than an assembly of niche markets. Organic wheat, for instance, is merely a niche in the much larger wheat market. In no part of agriculture is the line drawn more sharply than in corn production. Bt corn has become an anathema not only among organic consumers, but also in the consuming public at large.

Much the same is true of soybeans. Roundup Ready is not suitable for human consumption even though a great number of farmers have become entrapped by that technology.

In short, beans are not beans, beef is not beef and mutton is not mutton, these products taken as a bulk commodity. Nor is selling simply dumping the product on a market with no attention to needs, wants or the ability and willingness to pay a proper price.

Free-range pork is a niche sought in earnest by food afficionados. A countdown of hundreds of qualified organic products would serve no purpose except to eat up space. Prices of computer and internet applications would be more to the point. Suffice it to say that there is a domestic market for everything from elk antlers and Longhorn cattle horns and herbs for extraction and seasoning. In all cases the designation "pesticide free," "hormone free, *quality*, in short, trumps prices and synthetics any day of the week. How, then can an Internet venue assist a farmer in reading a satisfactory bottom line?

Used properly, here is a tool that enables transfer of product inventory information to a broad-spectrum audience detailing price, availability and shipment with the prospect of receiving instant response.

PRINCIPLES IN PLACE

In 1800, Alexandre and Susan Dugas Judice raised sugarcane in Iberia Parish, Louisiana, about 11 miles from the Gulf of Mexico. Five generations later, Joe and Gladys, and Robert and Pearl farm some of that same acreage. A sixth generation, Robert, Jr. and his wife Amy, became full partners in the farm in 1994. For now, these three couples and their children work together to carry on the family heritage of hard work, innovation and tending the land. Their success is rooted in the values of cooperation, stewardship, conservation, accurate accounting, and the creativity to live beyond survival.

"We're more efficient as a unity," claim Joe and Gladys. Joe explains that brother Robert excels in keeping up equipment – adapting machinery to better meet their needs and rebuilding to save the farm from investing in costly new equipment. According to Robert, Joe is good at keeping accurate records of their farming practices and on their land so they can make good business decisions.

Over the last 15 years the Judices have leased 450 acres to go with the 300 that they own. By handling less acreage than most, they are able to retain practices like hand planting and cover cropping. "As farms got big to produce in volume in hopes of surpassing production costs, cover cropping was forgotten," said Joe. "Farmers have too much land to farm and don't have time. We're fortunate we didn't have to work on such limited schedules. Our family has been cover cropping for over 50 years. It's a good practice. We always believed in putting back what we take out."

Most sugarcane farmers either chemically burn down or cultivate fallow fields in the fourth year of their rotation to prevent grasses and noxious weeds from flourishing. By growing soybeans every fourth year, the Judices add nitrogen to the soil, cut erosion and herbicide costs, and have an option of another cash crop when weather reduces their sugar harvest. "The cover crops pulled us through the bad years," says Joe. The Judices, like the generations before them, know hard work and sacrifices and don't regard either as unreasonable for the life they value — farming the land they love. But they also know that they must make time for their family in order to remain a strong family unit. They inherited this from their parents, Antoine and Marie.

Joe and Gladys say, "Land must be tended and nurtured and it will return to us what we need. It gives our family a sense of security and strong roots. It gives us a sense of belonging, a place in life, and reason to continue through disasters, low prices, and days when you just don't feel the result is worth the effort. It also gives us a sense of responsibility for our family's future generations. Land is like a young child, it is worth all the effort and care one gives to it. Together land and children are the most valuable resources we have."

With these principles in place, it is now correct to point out that there really is no need for a Board of Trade, a computerized crap game called the commodity market for sugar and soybeans and that production agriculture would better be served by a computer geared to private treaty trading.

THREE SHEPHERDS OF MAD RIVER VALLEY

The role of the innovator is difficult and laced with thorns. Institutional arrangements, especially government, seem dedicated to insuring failure, if not by subtle pressures, then by open warfare.

Three Shepherds farm was started in 1993, a transplant from England. The cast of characters, as this is written, were parents and children. The objective was milking sheep, cheese making, and family farming in an ecological way.

Larry Faillace has a Ph.D. in animal sciences. Linda handles marketing of breeding stock, cheese, and manages the farm store, office and European correspondence. Frances, at this writing age 16, handles pasture management and workaday sheep management. Heather, age 14, milks the sheep twice a day during milking season. Jackie, age 13, is America's youngest cheese maker.

Since milking sheep are all but unknown in the U.S., the family imported stock from Belgium herds, maintained under conditions better than most humans on planet Earth, USDA approved. A few years later officials concluded the herd had to be destroyed.

This brought friends and neighbors up fighting from their chairs. Government tests were suspect and pleas from the USDA that the court had no say so didn't wash with the judge.

Of interest here is not the rule on TSE and the tawdry business of feeding practices never used on the prize East Fresian sheep, but the principles involved to launch this unique farm.

Excellent cheese is hard to come by in the U.S. The idea of milking sheep is bound to spread if not cancelled out. As with grass-fed beef, there are opposing interests. Still, all the principles discussed in this book apply, including the electronic storefront, the on-scene store, the ecological approach. There is no room for corporate agriculture in Vermont, but there is lots of room for niche farms and niche merchandising.

The net reaches out and the customer enters the electronic storefront when the lightening strike of internet happens. Most important, the little guy can move as fast as the giant and often beat the Goliath. Three methods suggest themselves.

1. Commodities harvested and ready for market.
2. Commodities still growing or in storage.
3. Commodities represented as future production.

There are no less than four ways most of the hundreds of farm products can use and harvest Internet exposure.

1. *An interactive database for private treaty sales.* The interactive database involves buyers, sellers, contractees, contractors. In this case, all the above pay a membership fee. This enables the use of data, names, and passwords. Buyers post their credentials, bond numbers, etc. Anonymity is retained up to the point someone is ready to make a deal. Users in particular, find this device useful in identifying lot numbers, product identity and terms acceptable to the seller. Touching a "let's negotiate" button on the computer signals action potential. E-mail handles the message traffic.

2. *An Internet catalog.* The Internet catalog is not greatly different from the printed version. New software now makes it possible to write a negotiable check and transmit it by e-mail. For instance, a contract for, say, 5,000 bushels of soybeans suitable for tofu, delivery as stated, price as stated. The catalog is open for business 24 hours a day, 365 days a year. Here the buyers use a PIN (personal identification number), pushing the "buy" button. The database manager confirms. If the catalog fails, the product is released in time for sale in the regular market.

3. *An Internet auction.* Internet auctions require a database manager. Live auctions, Dutch auctions, all have rules and potential. The database management conducts the auction and takes a commission. Buyers have to be pre-qualified and bonded. Buyers and sellers are told by computers the outcome of the bidding. The buyer pays the freight and the customer directly. Descriptions always embody the jargon of the trade — for instance: lot #15, 15,000 bushels Jagger wheat, 12.75 protein, minimum price. The product can be handled as "in inventory" or "in the field," month of delivery designated.

4. *A farm website.* The fourth sales ticket depends on the website — the electronic store front. The goal here is to consummate private treaty sales for the individual, co-op or organization, usually by credit or debit card. The system is not unlike print advertisement, both for execution and results. All the elements of the classified ad surface on the site. Usually the customer downloads an order blank and mails in the request for a listed item. Comprehensive links to search engines need to be considered in setting up this store front.

These few notes are presented here as a hint that things are different in Century 21. Farmers have complete control, if they choose to exercise it. The farmer who thinks he or she is too old to learn might want to turn the computer chores over to the grandchildren.

The industrial directory aspect of the web may have great economic potential. Feedback suggests a new range of contacts, new buying and selling via the web. Publication of a web page by the farmer-entrepreneur suggests itself. It can announce for sale everything from kenaf and hogs to candled eggs and herb specialities. Buyers can thus find new sources of supply.

Some sites get a fantastic number of hits a day.

The interesting thing is that Internet operates on the existing infrastructure. The conduit to use is a provider. Once aboard for a fee each month, the user can transmit e-mail at no extra charge and read and explore to the heart's content.

A caution must be issued at this point. Nothing is very secret on the Internet. At any web site eavesdropping is possible. Indeed, a program for automatic interception is not only possible, it is probably a reality.

Nevertheless, an ISP (Internet Service Provider) and a modem on the computer for phone transmission has changed the business world in which we live. The sequence is simple: a software package connects to the ISP, and the ISP sends it to a destination. The equation reads: customer to ISP to ISP to customer. The receiving customer simply checks for messages the way one might go to a post office box.

E-mail and credit card business is now a fact of life.

Many farmer-entrepreneurs insist you can't run a profitable operation without computer assistance, and they may be right, if not now, then for the very near future.

The magic word is electronic store front.

The farm newsletter transmitted by e-mail is postage free under existing rules, and this is a working asset for farms such as Boggy Creek.

CHAPTER 18

Of Grasses & Grain

In the old South and up to the start of the Civil Rights movement, there was a saying, "white is right." A similar imperative presides over food production and marketing, even though it may not be as alliterative: "Science is right," and this right is furbished and refurbished by government clout, intellectual corruption and business skulduggery. I cannot detain the reader with chapter and verse on hundreds of farm products, therefore a short pass at meat protein and genetic engineering will have to make the point. First, the scientific system is superb when unclouded by political and business considerations. But as huckstered today it is the god that failed. The fallout has contaminated minds, water, soil and food.

Former President Jimmy Carter regurgitated the conventional ignorance on genetic engineering in an Op-Ed article for major dailies. It was the official spin of USDA, Extension, the university system and the food giants. It was the position Dennis Avery handed off in *Saving the Planet with Pesticides and Plastic: The Environmental Triumph of High-Yield Farming*. Science, he wrote, was doing nothing farmers haven't been doing for thousands of years. They cross-bred the best to the best. Thus, they helped evolve superior strains of corn, wheat, apples, etc.

The reason for being of the organic movement answers this distortion of the truth. That answer enlarges criticisms of meat protein production called "conventional" expressed earlier, but also poses more than a few questions about the traditional way of doing business, a culture that too often fails to produce a satisfactory bottom line.

Ted Slanker, a Red River Valley (Texas) cattleman who relies solely on grass to feed his animals, has shared with me much of his insight, 13 points we are required to consider at the end of this chapter.

He, Oklahoma's Jim Lents, and several dozen red meat producers are all agreed that genetic engineering threatens beef production from without while bad genetics, husbandry and business practices threaten it from within. The victims are producers and consumers alike. The farmers do not comprehend the finer points of their craft; the latter do not understand the science gone wrong that threatens their very existence.

Most cow-calf operators sell their calves at weaning. And most cow-calf operators are small, usually averaging no more than 20 head. Management practices are high cost, dependent on supplementation, vet services, hay, cubes and protein licks. Even calves get grain, often genetically modified grain pronounced unsuitable for human consumption.

To recite anew how studies become scientific reports which become wisdom would seem to be a reflection on the intelligence of the reader. Still it is well to note that educators speak as with a single voice. Indeed, their livelihood depends on this discipline — educators are not risk takers.

Fragments of knowledge can stand alone, but to be meaningful, they must be integrated into a system. Political correctness does not answer this requirement.

No single development of the past 20 or 30 years illustrates this point more than cross-breeding — if that term can be allowed — at the molecular level. Organic producers must understand the grammar of this subject or their movement will be swallowed the way large commodity producers are being swallowed by larger (often foreign) competitors.

The human body has ten million million cells. Each cell has a specific job to do. Cells form tissues and organs. Cells reproduce, create their own kind and die. The control center is called the nucleus. Herein resides the cell's genetic program. The nucleus contains chromosomes and nuclei. Chromosomes are thread-like structures composed of DNA — deoxyribonucleic acid — and certain proteins.

DNA is a blueprint of sorts. It tells cells how to divide and reproduce copies of themselves. Picture a twisted rope ladder. All DNA structures are shaped this way — on a flower, a dog, a human being.

The rungs of the ladder are made up of four components, adenine, cytosine, guanine and thymine. These are usually written as A, G, C and T. A can only pair with T, and C with G. Base pairs reproduce themselves, and that is where genetic manipulation enters the scene. Millions of these base pairs form genes. Evolution has taken up the chore of detecting the base pair reproduction, frequently and even usually improving the life structure. Genetic engineers have learned how to add and delete from the ladder. They came by this knowledge in the following way.

An Austrian monk named Gregor Mendel hinted at the direction for research, but it remained for Frederich Griffith, a British microbiologist, to discern what was later identified as DNA. In the early 1950s, Maurice Wilkins and Rosalind Franklin at the King's College in England used x-ray refraction photography to study DNA. They came up with an outline of the DNA molecule. The Nobel Prize would have gone to Franklin except for her untimely death. Nobel Prizes are awarded only to living persons. Using Franklin's work as background, James Watson and Francis Crick, working at Cambridge, constructed a model of DNA, the double helix. In 1953, Wilkins joined Watson and Crick in receiving the Nobel Prize.

It was a small step to discover naturally occurring enzymes that act like molecular scissors for the purpose of adding or deleting rungs from the DNA ladder.

Breaking the molecule has been applauded because of the potential for fighting hereditary disease conditions. Use of the technology has permitted laboratories to manufacture things like insulin. Thus was born the idea of cutting and recombining at the molecular level. Thus was born the idea of finding a trait in one organism and transferring it to another organism. Thus also was born the idea of engineering the totality of life.

GRASS INTO BEEF

Ask Allan Nation, editor of *Stockman's Grass Farmer,* for an opinion and he'll tell you unequivocally that Gordon Hazard is the king of low-input agriculture. All any grazier really needs, according to Gordon, is a little pickup truck. Hazard readily admits to making extremely good money with his all-grass farm near West Point, Mississippi; however, he remembers lean times. He is the son of an Iowa crop farmer who lost it all when he moved south to till the thin, black soil of Mississippi. That left Gordon Hazard skeptical of black dirt and plows.

Gordon has found he can grow excellent crops of fescue, dallies, Bermuda, white clover and lespedeza on the Mississippi prairie. Turning this grass into beef has allowed Gordon to accumulate some 3,000 acres of "white soil" and a totally paid for base herd of about 1,800 stocker cattle. He has been a debt-free farmer since the 1970s.

He winters his cattle using fall-stockpiled fescue and no hay or feed. Dallis and lespedeza provide most of his summer grazing, and he is pleased with a sub-clover/annual ryegrass/crabgrass system he has worked out for his sandy soils. He has found that subclover needs a good annual disking to reseed and compete with volunteer grasses. This also promotes a crabgrass crop the following May when the subclover goes dormant. This subclover/crabgrass double crop is producing the highest gains per acre and per head on his farm.

Gordon prefers the stocker business to a cow/calf operation because it is more flexible and fast-paced. He said stocking was virtually a no-risk enterprise if you could grow quality pasture and if you structure the business well financially. He buys calves year-round, depending upon their price and his grass conditions. He has never used the futures market. He says, "I make my money in this business by producing beef from grass, not gambling on the price of cattle."

While Gordon is no longer interested in expanding his holdings, he is helping his children get into ranching. He said, "I think 1,500 to 1,800 steers is a nice size grass operation for one man. You can make an excellent living from it and it is still small enough to be hassle-free."

Plant breeding is slow work. In the meantime, the population time bomb is ticking. That's the premier argument for fast-track use of genetic engineering in crop production, hang the dangers and the consequences. But history reveals that the fast track in science is full of potholes and axle-breaking bumps. *Acres U.S.A.* has recited some of the problems, as was the case when L-Tryptophan, made with genetically modified organisms, was green-lighted into trade channels. The horror stories attached to the use of Bt corn and Roundup Ready soybeans are stacking up like cordwood. The anomalies brought on by consuming genetically modified potatoes are now a matter of record.

The debate is emerging from the shadows. In the case of BGH — bovine growth hormone — citizens generally vote with their dollars to reject the "shooting from the hips" assurances of officialdom. The brashest of the engineers look to designing animals and even infants. Ethical considerations are either ignored or swept aside.

As with DDT and atomic hazards, the voice of the people has still to be heard. Splicing human genetic material into a hog has no ethical implications for some modern Neanderthalers, but it is something we all need to think about. There are too many people who rarely trouble themselves thinking about ethics, or consequences.

There are probably over 15,000 people on the Extension payroll, hundreds if not a thousand "agents" included. Why then, is it necessary for organic farmers to virtually go it alone, helped only by a few stray advisers and journals?

Ted E. Slanker, Jr. writes the controversial "Just Managing to Get By" beef cattle management column that appears in several Midwest papers. The column's focus is profitability, consequently he discusses various management approaches. His emphasis is managing cow-calf operations without the input costs usually associated with the business, supplements, vet bills, hay, etc. Rotational grazing figures and grass is king, as well as "the forgiveness of nature, her constant benediction," to quote John J. Ingalls, the old-time Kansas Senator. Salad mix pastures and proven genetics are his forte. Proper use of EPDs, better health programs, marketing programs and alliances, all figure. The list seems endless. At the drop of a hat, Ted will discuss winter stocker pastures, a 45-day breeding period, handling cattle via land without dogs or horses, fencing off ponds, whatever. Selling grass fed beef to grocery stores has been and remains an objective.

Everything stated in this book argues for change in order to achieve optimum results. Political correctness is promoted by the existing order to safeguard its investment in what "works today," meaning it has so far evaded convulsion. Change devalues such an indictment and is therefore discouraged.

The above stated in terms of the grass fed beef producer settles down to 13 points, and these points more or less define the dilemma of the farmer in any operation when honed and shaped by real analysis.

1. *Packers,* who have expensive plants located too far from the best grass-growing regions of the country.

2. *Feeders,* who own feedlots that currently feed all of the nation's young cattle that go to slaughter.

3. *Stocker operators,* thousands of whom purchase calves to put on winter wheat.

4. *Grain growers,* who have large investments in machinery and facilities to raise and ship huge volumes of product to the feedlots and cow-calf producers.

5. *Feed mills and feed stores,* which are dependent on cattlemen supplementing their cattle.

6. *Drug companies,* which may experience a drop in sales if cattle are healthier on grass than they are in the feedlots. (They will certainly lose a lot of hormone implant business if producers leave their bulls intact and market them as all natural, grass-fed beef.)

7. *Our nation's health industry,* which is larger and more costly than it has ever been before and which primarily treats health problems related to diets heavy in bad fats. (Better diets mean fewer health problems and less business.)

8. *Food processors and manufacturers,* which will face embarrassment and lost sales as new nutritional guidelines kill off previously successful products.

9. *Food retailers,* which will be reluctant at first to switch to, or even introduce, new products for fear of losing business on mainstream products.

10. *Projects sponsored by, and employees of the Beef Checkoff,* which will see a drastic reduction in funding if most calves are retained rather than sold. (Additionally, the Beef Checkoff will find it nearly impossible to market grain-fed and grass-fed beef at the same time, so it will try to stick with what works for now.)

11. *Sale barns,* which will experience a major reduction in the number of cattle marketed if producers switch to marketing direct through meat marketing alliances.

12. *Producers,* who can be the main beneficiaries of the grass-fed management and marketing approach yet will still ridicule and stonewall grass-fed beef because the entire approach will be foreign to them and they just don't like change.

13. *Educators,* who have been teaching old practices but will feel foolish teaching new practices they once ridiculed. (Also, when educators start to teach new grazing and grass-fed approaches they will have to downsize because of the grass-fed beef raising and marketing approach.)

AN ECOLOGICAL FARM

Duane Hager likes to think of himself as an average Minnesota dairy farmer. In many ways he is, but he is far ahead of the crowd by farming ecologically. Both he and his father before him have farmed without toxic pesticides and herbicides – adding up to about 50 years of clean land stewardship.

Duane farms 220 acres near the southeastern Minnesota town of Kellogg, close to the scenic bluffs along the Mississippi River. His land has soil types ranging from sandy to heavy clay. He raises corn, soybeans, oats and hay (alfalfa plus orchardgrass and timothy).

As he has taken rented land that had been farmed conventionally and converted it to biologically active land; Duane has been fascinated by the visible changes and improvements. Without toxic chemicals and strong salt fertilizers, earthworms soon increase dramatically, along with a noticeable improvement in soil health. In 1993, the day after a four-inch rain, he was able to drive on a field that had many worm castings without mud sticking to his tractor tires.

Duane relies on judiciously applied manure for much of his crop nutrition, along with corn and alfalfa starter fertilizers. He collects dairy manure in a liquid storage pit and spreads it in the fall. His manure collection method is a less common gravity-flow system. He has another pit for solid manure from feed lots, and he can spread it at various times, giving him more flexibility.

The 40 Holstein and Guernsey cows are milked in a tie-stall barn. During the warm months, the dairy cattle eat green-chopped hay and are pastured on rotational grazing. In the winter, the cows stay in the barn and get corn silage and baled hay. Milk production runs around a 15,500 rolling herd average, with 3.5 to 4.1 percent butterfat and 3.2 percent protein. Duane has won milk quality awards form his dairy in past years. Keeping the ration adjusted for changing feeds is always a challenge, he noted.

Duane also raises about 30 beef cattle, either Angus, Hereford or Angus-Hereford cross.

This farm is correctly positioned for the innovative structure now abounding in eco-agriculture.

Bluntly stated, the farmers to whom this book is addressed are mavericks largely operating in a free market. Market orders can and do break organic producers, raisin-grape growers for instance, and Extension workers who criticize Dennis Avery and Hudson Food can be fired summarily. But in the main, the niche producer enjoys a large measure of freedom.

As eco-farming and business prove themselves, educators will pick up the guidance. In the meantime, the reasons for rejection provide a good "for instance."

The cross-currents are powerful, not only for beef, but also for dairy, fruits, vegetables. The bottom line question is simply, who is to benefit from the work of the farmer?

Business principles are not economic principles. In the last chapter I will ask you to join me in a mental helicopter for an overview of the system in which we live. All will be telescoped into a simple equation over which government presides. The abstraction is not difficult. Simply set aside preconceived ideas and open your mind to an overview that admits very little influence by the individual except as an aggregate.

It will be seen that although we live and work under the umbrella of an economy, the principles that govern the whole are often exactly opposite the principles that preside over the Darwinian landscape called business enterprise. This is the reason governments are instituted among men, hopefully with ethical and moral content in tow. In Andrew Jackson's day, it was widely proclaimed that "the *Bible* is the foundation on which the Republic rests." We are allowed to question this diction for our time's transnationals view the world as their country, borders merging no more than longitude and latitude lines on a Mercator projection. Some understanding of the overview is necessary if the businessman-farmer is to navigate his or her way to a business bottom line, whatever the general drift of the economy. We will now set aside the lessons of this little book and take that aerial view, always cognizant that a fire on our Hinderberg can close many a shop, the least vulnerable being the bottom line farmer.

CHAPTER 19

Economics & Business

In the opening chapter of this book, I asked the question, What was it about agriculture that made it both the curse and the blessing of mankind? The perceptive reader will wonder aloud whether what followed in fact supplied an answer.

There was a time some 40 years ago, when many of the farmers cited in this *Guide* sought to achieve a better bottom line by changing the institutional arrangements under which they farmed. This led to the study of economics and a realization that institutions are quite intractable. I was aboard when the NFO launched its milk holding action in 1967, and I joined the leadership in a Des Moines courtroom when the government closed down the action. Later a consent decree announced to the world that public policy would never give farmers the one thing they were entitled to, first crack at the American market.

Del Akerlund of Valley, Nebraska was an officer in NFO at the time. When the great movement was emasculated by the federal courts, which allowed it to exist only as a shell, Del and his brother Val decided to farm smart in a business sense, and let public policy proceed on its own dumb course.

Francis Polifka, an eco-grower from near Catharine, Kansas, has followed a similar orientation. In both of these cases, both farms continue to monitor the general economic scheme of things, even though they have opted for the shelter of the media rather than the protection of the public policy.

An understanding of broad-spectrum economics is essential for the farmer who has still to understand why he must become a farmer-entrepreneur. The arbitrary point at which I will start is base period 100, 1948, the year during which Congress passed the basic legislation under which we operated until 1996. It was the end of World War II. A new economic theory period was being pushed forward, one that stated as an absolute truth the proposition that food is much like any other product, and that farming governed by technology is the same as manufactures. This truth holds as new technology is introduced, enhanced productivity and technology must follow as night the day. The bottom line is that high science and technology will produce more food at cheaper prices, and therefore benefit the economy here and people everywhere. This model, the conventional truth held, will be drawn capillary-style to the far corners of the world. The elimination of excess people from farming is no different, this argument holds, than the passing of the buggy whip factory. Finally, this singsong argument has it, "How you going to keep them down on the farm after they've seen Paree?" As with many so-called obvious truths, this one has proved to be hopelessly false. It fails to comply with the laws of thermodynamics, sociology and economics.

In order to get to the point in a minimum of time and space, I ask you to consider what might pass for a transparency in a lecture. I am doing this because I have to posture the whole of agriculture in the national exchange equation.

Using the structure of the *Economic Indicators* and the one found in *The Economic Report of the President*, I have determined both the national income and its component parts.

National Income

Agriculture Corporations Small Business & Services Rentals	Wages & Supplements Interest
$33\frac{1}{3}$ percent	**$66\frac{2}{3}$ percent**

Some of you will know that this general schematic was developed by the late Simon Kuznets, who won a Nobel Prize for his work with economic statistics. He reasoned, correctly I believe, that in a private enterprise economy these component parts line themselves up as an equation, with the private enterprise sectors furnishing the income to satisfy the costs of operating the economy. The basics can be seen below.

Please note that for the economy to stay solvent based on the present state of the arts, the income side of the equation must earn approximately $33\frac{1}{3}$ percent of the national income in order to pay the costs, namely wages and supplements and interest to persons. This assumes, of course, that it is the public policy objective of the nation to enjoy full employment, a relatively stable price level — not pummeled by inflation — and an absence of stability-destroying import invasion. Needless to say, there would be no policy for public and private debt exponential growth.

To make what I am saying comprehensible, I must now point out that economics has no year 0, as does history, generally accepted as the date of the birth of Christ. Therefore, economists have to select a base period usually styled as 100, from which to proceed forward or look back. Such a base period should comply with the norms imposed by public policy. Public policy can order full employment or abject poverty. It can reward incentive or punish it. It can give the fruits of the economy's labor to a few, or prescribe parity for the many.

There have been three excellent base periods equaling 100 in all of Century 20 that made possible balanced budgets without depressions, with full employment and with the other norms treasured by a mature society: 1910-1914, 1926-1929, and 1947-1949. Whenever the profit side of the national income equation does not earn enough to support the cost side based on the percent one-third to two-thirds ratio required by the state of the arts, the shortage on the income side of the equation will equal the annual expansion in the public and private debt. The cumulative shortfall of income to the four private enterprise sectors always equals the total public and private debt, now trillions of dollars.

The cost sector is generally defined by the standard of living. The income sector is now determined by the lowest common denominator in international trade channels. This brings the appropriate lineup as follows.

In order to synthesize national prosperity, public policy has hit agriculture hardest and is well into the business of annihilating many aspects of private enterprise as well, substituting debt for earnings in the process. Those who bother to reason from physics rather than from the money mendacity of the merchant have concluded that all energy and matter come from nature, generally from the raw materials of the earth. The metabolic and kinetic energy requirements of the population and industry — the raw materials, in short — as monetized at the first point of sale, determine the national income on an earned basis. By using the data from

TUCKASEGEE GINSENG

All over the Appalachian region there are small towns that are home to ginseng brokers. In Scott Persons' town of 20,000, Tuckasegee, North Carolina, there are two sellers of what Scott calls "green gold." Scott Persons knows so much about American ginseng that he wrote a book entitled *American Ginseng: Green Gold.* It is, according to Persons, a high-value, high-risk crop. He grows his own wild-simulated ginseng crop.

"There is no good way to plant ginseng," he says. But the "quick and dirty" method he uses is to mark off a 40-foot by 50-foot woodland area, and clear the area of dead limbs and saplings. "What you want," he says, "is a nice forest with herbal undergrowth and a slope, if possible" After clearing, leaves are raked aside and the top inch of soil loosened by hand raking methods. He then hand casts seed and rakes it into the ground. The final steps are to carefully rake the leaves back over the ground to protect the seeds from moisture loss, and then, perpendicular to the slope, place the limbs and saplings to hold everything in place. With any luck, 25 to 35 percent of the seeds will germinate and you hope for one plant per square foot of land.

According to Scott, "The wonderful thing about growing ginseng is that it's so easy to sell. But it's very hard to grow." What you get for your trouble are prices anywhere from $225 per pound to over $300 for wild ginseng. That's a lot of money, but the risks are high since you wait six years for the return on your investment, and through all six seasons you sweat it out with nature. Since pathogens are less virulent in a forest environment, pests are not a huge problem. The most difficult plant problem with cultivated ginseng are foliar- and root-related fungi because the plant is susceptible to fungi to begin with and the conditions required for ginseng growing promote fungus growth. However, the woods provide better air circulation and fungus problems are less troublesome.

Poachers really present the greatest threat to ginseng growers in his region. People know the value of the product and are not above stealing it. One grower he knows solved his poaching problems by raising an additional crop around his ginseng plot – he raises attack dogs for sale.

Withal, the bottom line comes into view when buyers find the source, and the source markets in a business-like way.

many federal agencies, it has been determined that raw material's income times the state-of-the-arts multiplier of approximately 7.30 equals the earned national income. Any additional national income has to be generated by debt.

These few observations require me to detail how agriculture was subjected to near total debauchery by the postwar farm act passed in 1948 (generally called the Farm Act of 1949). This act subjected American farm production values to world price pressures, especially storable farm commodities. Importation of even one or two percent of a basic crop in terms of domestic production was enough to make it impossible for farmers Akerlund and Polifka to achieve a satisfactory bottom line, and there seemed to be little organization could do about it.

Some few farmers tried to rescue themselves with new business efficiency and dangerous alchemy. These technologies, pressured into existence by public policy, removed from trade channels almost all forms of wholesome meat, grains and vegetables. The conceit that modern agriculture is more productive is based entirely on the proposition that it uses less labor. By any other standard of measurement — production per acre, units of energy consumed, by relative capital input — the small farm wins hands down. Nevertheless, the public policy has chased the less labor delusion, and even exported it regardless of social costs. The objective of achieving the greatest weight gain over the shortest period of time first captured the imagination of the poultry industry. Grains became recognized as the reason for being of "economy of scale" expansion, and cardboard tasting vegetables canceled out local farmers and handed "sourcing" to Mexico, foreign climes, and hardly more than four southern and western states.

Readers may wonder why and how the above quite simple national equation was set aside, and for what purpose the destruction of the family farm is being pursued as a matter of public policy. Surely the primacy of raw materials from earth, sea and sky best complies with the reality of planet life, production and commerce. Economists, political people, even common workers scoff at this assessment, the former because they have a package to sell, the latter because they have bought that package even though it is inimical to their best interest. The package that presumes to vacate the primacy of raw materials is called *trade*. Trade between the several peoples on planet earth is said to hold the "key to peace on earth," general prosperity for all, and it is set out as a solution to practically everything. The primacy of free international trade is so self-evident, the schoolmen say, all this fundamentalism about the raw products of the earth and the physical economy isn't worth talking about. Having been beaten around the head and shoulders by academia for several decades, it occurs to me that a new attempt at explanation should be made now that the above equations have been restated.

"Don't even try," one schoolman told me. "God is dead and it is no

THE PHYSICAL ECONOMY

FARM

TRACTOR DEALER

FARMER
Sells wheat
& buys
tractor

MILL

TRACTOR MANUFACTURER

MILLER

BAKER

BAKERY

STORE
KEEPER

BREAD

CONSUMER

STORE

use appealing to order in the universe. We rely on science these days." Anyone can finish that sentence in 25 words or less.

The relationship between the cycles that govern the arrival of energy — kinetic and metabolic — can be explained, albeit not in 25 words, and the primacy of that event trails to the multiple of activities until that energy is finally spent. Most of the confusion in economics is born of the inability to comprehend proximate cause and primary cause.

It is probably redundant to probe back to a big bang or even Aristotle's First Cause. It appears that the Creator's design calls for Jupiter and Saturn to cause an imbalance in the solar system. This tampers with the magnetic forces operative in the upper layers of the sun.

Calculations have it that the sun's output could fall up to two percent. Such a drop in mean temperatures would have the effect of moving all farms above the Equator some 300 miles north. The effect on crop production can be imagined. It happened in 1630, and 1810. Extreme cold prompts people to migrate. During the Little Ice Age, dynasties were overthrown and food shortages caused civil unrest. Sunspots govern crop failure or bounty. Cycle watchers nowadays point to the most important cycles — the 11.1- to 11.2-year sunspot cycle, for instance. Many reach their low point in the first years of Century 21.

Crop production supplies the mechanism for national solvency, just as sunspots govern crop failure or bounty. W. Stanley Jevons discovered the sunspot periodicity during the 18th Century. He found that when the spots diminished, it caused cosmic nourishment to fall off, and weather to subtract favor from crop production. Other cycles plug in from time to time, the basic one dealing with the arrival of metabolic energy for the human machine. The arrival of the exchange mechanism pointed those who could reason correctly to production as the author of income, albeit only after monetized by price. No production times whatever the price still means no income. Simple exchanges add to the price but not to the gross domestic product.

The first principle became transparently obvious once it had been stated. Trade created no overall economic income unless the buyer or seller cheated. Gambling created nothing and served only to transfer money from one pocket to the next. It was the capacity of institutional arrangements to intervene in the process that brought on depressions and hard times as long as the cycles of nature did not decree otherwise. It was the primacy of nature's gifts that suggested the foundational ideas ultimately expressed in Kuznet's statistics and formulas.

Now that borrowing and creating money out of thin air has become the norm, it seems useless to argue against the efficiency of the system before it self-destructs. This event, the cycles say, will take place early in Century 21.

Those who fought for parity during the '50s, '60s and '70s can be allowed to wonder, what would have happened if excessive debt had been outlawed, and a balanced federal budget mandated? What would have been the result if the lessons of World War II had been heeded?

We really do not need to speculate because we have the record to rely on, elements of which were published as early as 1944 in *Country Gentlemen* magazine, and further codified since then by NORM and in my books, *Unforgiven* and *Raw Materials Economics*. As early as the 1930s, research revealed that the United States could have any level of prosperity it decided without the threatening cataclysm of debt simply by maintaining farm and raw materials income on par with cost factors in the rest of the economy. Indeed, data reaching back to the beginning of the republic proved beyond a shadow of doubt that appropriate farm and raw product income were the guarantees of full factory employment and national prosperity. All the major interests in the United States economy are governed by this factor — if law and institutional arrangements prohibit reliance on fiat money and reckless termination of the provisions of our constitution.

The value of manufactures — labor payrolls, retail sales, transportation income, the volume of construction — all are limited by raw materials income. They follow at an interval of a few months. Indeed, the national balance sheet is always regulated by the raw materials of the earth multiplied by the prices they command, a natural law requirement that cannot be set aside without unsound debt creation.

All the above findings emerged in 1944 from studies conducted under the auspices of the National Association of Commissioners, Secretaries and Directors of Agriculture (NASDA). NASDA commissioned the study because they wanted to know how it was possible to create the income needed to make full employment and the distribution of factory goals possible. The researchers were Carl H. Wilken, Charles Ray, and former Tariff Commission Chairman, John Lee Coulter. It probably never occurred to any of them that one day scholars would talk about baseball teams or gambling boats generating earned income for the system, or that debt would be substituted for earnings, or that doubling and redoubling of debt was a continuing possibility.

It was known during the 19th and early 20th Centuries that farm income was a barometer of purchasing power. Summed up, the Wilken, Ray and Coulter findings revealed that raw materials income, chiefly that of agriculture, is a prime mover in the national economy. A by-product of the above-named research was the discovery of a natural law, a law of exchange which controlled the complex system by which we live. Raw materials income starts the cycle, the researchers said. "It is the new wealth annually created by production. All other money involved in the process of manufactures and delivery to the consumer is money temporarily borrowed from the store of capital already in existence, and is returned to it when the finished goods are sold." It is the rate of turnover of raw materials income as it passes through the various stages of economic use that is the key.

The NASDA researchers found that there is a rate of turnover to this raw materials income as it passes through the several stages of economic use. Wilken put it this way. "The national income on an earned basis is simply the amount of raw materials income times the rate of turnover. The nation's wage fund, the manufacturing output possible, and the amount of public purchasing power are fixed by the turn of raw materials dollars." This turn is a multiplier governed by the state of the arts.

Going back into the records for nearly a century, the researchers found this natural law constantly at work setting the limits of the national income on an earned basis. The rule has not changed, but the multiplier has emerged as a moving constant regulated by changes in technology and sophistication of the economic process. In 1850, approximately half our labor force was required in the production of raw materials. The turnover or multiplier was only two. By 1925 to 1929, the national efficiency had risen enough to establish a multiplier of 3.9. By the end of World War II, a five-fold turn emerged from the statistical arrays. According to research sponsored by National Organization for Raw Materials (NORM), the raw materials multiplier is now approximately 7.30 and is likely to remain near 7.30 during the first quarter of Century 21.

ALWAYS SOMETHING GREEN

"Always something green" is the philosophy Nathan Jones, King's Crown Organic Farm, King Hill, Idaho, has about farming organically. His 400 acres produce alfalfa, pastures, dry beans, onions, garlic, winter squash, watermelon, and even Chardonnay grapes — all certified organic. He started with organic garlic, wanting a high value cash crop. He calls that first experience his "tuition," because from it he learned "you better have a market before you grow anything." That first crop of garlic was beautiful, but without a marketing strategy Nathan lost money.

Nate first made the switch to organic in the late 1980s and, while he doesn't recommend "jumping in with both feet" as he did, his "yields were initially the same and then immediately got better" than they were with conventional methods. A crop rotation system of alfalfa, beans, vegetable crop, onions, beans, alfalfa is used on the farm and cover crops are planted — there is always something growing. Weeds are managed through a winter cover of rye and hand weeding. "We cultivate and pre-irrigate to help control weeds." His inputs are green manure, compost, soft rock phosphate, kelp and a fish product, and humic acid.

For Nate Jones the move to organic is a trade-off. He says money spent on chemicals is now spent on labor for the intensive farming methods he uses. However, he notes that it's beneficial in the long run because he hires local labor, who work for him and keep the money in the area. He has a family working for him who are now "in tune with the crops," so he's motivated to keep them on.

His product often sells itself. He says, "We farmers are always trying to get the buyer to call us and that's the ultimate. At least right now, they call and ask me how much I want and they buy it. I can almost get emotional about it. A lot of farmers work all their lives and never experience this."

Academia slaps its sides in bellowing amusement at this finding, relying on the delusion created by debt injections. These schoolmen can "prove" a national income well above the one claimed for the raw materials multiplier. Nevertheless, in terms of a stable dollar, the natural law described above holds.

The delusion marches in all directions. The work force engaged in agriculture and raw materials is vastly lower than the raw materials extended to earned national income suggests. The shortfall is almost exactly the standing unemployment figure, and the institutionalized poverty flowing therefrom. The rest of the population is able to earn a living by taking the raw materials to the factory, processing them, distributing the finished goods and performing other services called for by our standard of living. In an economy that elects to operate on an earned basis, the amount of raw materials production — farm production being primary — and the price it brings determines the amount of national income that can be distributed among the several groups illustrated in the T chart exhibited above. The new income this provides is a starter for the whole machinery of exchange. If in balance with cost factors, the machine goes full speed. If raw materials — especially farm products — are underpriced, the machine slows down and bad times follow. Expanded debt, public and private, can halt the inevitable result, but for a time only.

Agriculture supplies between two-thirds and 70 percent of their starter income. It is the most sensitive because the product is quickly consumed and has to be replaced. The income from hard commodities such as iron, copper, stone, etc., enters the exchange equation more slowly. This reality was cemented into place once upon a time because agriculture accounted for broad-spectrum distribution of income among vastly greater numbers of communities and peoples. The proof of this thesis can be seen when we examine what happens in the absence of debt injection. For instance, farm production in 1928 and 1932, when the raw materials off the farm was approximately the same each year, but the market value was cut in half in 1932, the national income also dropped by half and the raw materials multiplier remained the same. Factory payrolls took a similar drop. Specifically, acute production fell twice as much, and construction almost vanished. When farm income moved up, the other sectors followed. Thus, it seems a failure to maintain a flow of new income charts the road to perdition.

Consumers in the aggregate do not gain from low farm prices. They always spend a greater percentage of their real income for food when farm prices are low. Charlatans always sell inflation as the way out, and most people like it at first. We now live in $100,000 homes and we didn't even have to move.

The swing of the stars seems to bring mathematical ambition to term with physical reality. Something happens in the ozone and ion exchange. Cool weather energizes people. They strike off the chains of oppression.

A heavy dose of reality sets in. Welfare governments discover they can't tax enough to pay for a parasite overload. For now, it seems self-evident the American people can eat and digest a great deal more inflation. They can't eat and digest the type of provender toxic technology has accounted for.

Public policy's failure requires the farmer to go for it — it being the business answer to an economic dilemma. In the worst of times and in the best of times, business proceeds. The food business of Century 21 will turn slowly to what we now call organics. Lee Fryer, in *An Organic Manifesto*, has described how much of the vegetable produce on grocery store racks is unspeakably contaminated. Earlier in this book, I related how poultry is grown, the result being that most of it is unfit to eat. Artificial growth hormones, antibiotics, anti-coccidials to treat fungal infections, and genetically-modified foods are the norm. Chickens that arrive at the kitchen have 1,000 percent more fat than free-roaming counterparts such as those grown on the Troque Farm, Buckner Missouri.

This and other inventories of information in the foregoing chapters contains its own suggestions. Animal agriculture is an important foundation stone for the income side of the national equation. It is being endangered by the technological trap into which it has fallen.

For now it is enough to observe that the failure of the meat protein industry to supply a fresh, wholesome food product will lead to a diminished industry for two reasons.

The balance between organic production and demand is heavily weighed on the demand side as I set down these lines. Organic grocery stores are springing up. Restaurants will follow and are following.

In the wake of these developments, government elects to stay the course, never questioning the "economy of scale" idea, always demanding that bigger and bigger farmers produce more and more for less and less, until bankruptcy consumes them all. Yet there is a bottom line. Those who find it "get smart." Any size farm will do, as long as a plan presides, and as long as the old "what'll you give me?" penchant goes out the window. After all, the people who gave the country its present macroeconomic plan also gave it toxic technology. Those who have specialized in being wrong won't help you. Those who have backgrounded the lessons contained in this *Guide* and in *Acres U.S.A.* hold in escrow the answers. Help yourself.

Consumer demand will vanish perceptibly as buyers either reject the product — perhaps only one percent a year at a time — either because they are no longer satisfied with tasteless, grease-laden, health-destroying fare, or because they do not have the ability to buy. The ability to buy, I have pointed out, is governed by the ability of the private enterprise sector to pay wages once the credit device fails. The economic equation won't be denied.

Afterword

Innovation and change are bitter enemies, intractable enemies that behave like dogs in the manger. Tradition is always something of value that needs to be replaced before it is discarded. The values that nature has bestowed can be hardly displaced by psuedo science and crass commercialism. It is the traditional concept of business that cries out for remedy.

If you take a printed picture and examine it closely, you'll discover that it isn't a picture at all, rather a concentration of pixels — dots of various sizes — juxatoposed to create shades and textures, dark spots and light spots. Propinquity of pixels governs. Pull out a cluster of dots and the picture changes.

The purpose here has been to deal with the dots and small clusters of what is euphemistically called the market, the business and the economy. I think of each farm as a niche and the sale of the farm's production as a niche market. Production is only a part of the farmer's task.

There are plenty of people who know precisely how to order the economy so as to give the commodity producer a fair break in what we call the traditional market. Unfortunately, they do not have the job.

The Freedom to Farm Act passed the baton back to the individual pixel in the picutre. The USDA has defined many of those pixels out of the picture because they aren't big enough to answer the bureaucratic criterion of what contitutes a farm. Nevertheless, those pixel-farmers can find the few dozen or hundred customers they need to make a living. Each has a different set of circumstances, resrouces, spark of energy. Each has to take the situation by the seat of the pants and nape of the neck and shake out results.

If any of these ideas and vignettes have inspired or helped, I consider myself amply rewarded.

Acknowledgments

My intention has been to amply acknowledge all contributors in the text itself. One glaring omission remains — the acknowledgment due to staffers of *Acres U.S.A.* for all the work involved in bringing this work into print. The vignettes used to punctuate these pages have been mined largely fromthe pages of *Acres U.S.A.* and structured on the basis of personal interviews.

Many thanks to the following people, each of whom advised, wrote, or otherwise contributed to the profiles in this book: Paul and Nancy Jones Keiser, Paul Crawford, Rob Johnson, Bob Shaffer, Harold Willis, Dick Richardson, Ann Ruggles, Jody Butterfield, Keith Richards, Hugh Lovel, Phil Callahan, Eric Ardapple Kindberg, Archer Christian, Margaret Merrill, John Brown, Steven Kendall, Lee Fryer, Fred Wood, Malcolm Beck, Bargyla Rateaver, Richard Alan Miller, Allan Nation, Lydia Poulsen, Lorna McMahon, Andy Lopez, Howard Garrett, Harold Wills, E.O. McDonagh, and Eric Gibson.

Finally, I want to thank Anna Ross for the valued assistance she has conferred on this one last book.

APPENDIX A

PROPRIETORSHIP — COMPILED,
ACCRUAL BASIS,
COMPARATIVE FINANCIAL STATEMENTS
WITH FULL DISCLOSURES

A. B. JOHNSON COMPANY

FINANCIAL STATEMENTS

Years Ended December 31, 19X2 and 19X1

(ACCOUNTANT'S LETTERHEAD)

Mr. A. B. Johnson A. B. Johnson Company Lawton, Oklahoma

I have compiled the accompanying balance sheets of A. B. Johnson Company (a proprietorship) as of December 31, 19X2 and 19X1, and the related statements of income and proprietor's capital and cash flows for the years then ended, in accordance with Statements on Standards for Accounting and Review Services issued by the American Institute of Certified Public Accountants.

A compilation is limited to presenting in the form of financial statements information that is the representation of the owner. I have not audited or reviewed the accompanying financial statements and, accordingly, do not express an opinion or any other form of assurance on them.

(Firm's signature)

February 15, 19X3

A. B. JOHNSON COMPANY
BALANCE SHEETS
December 31, 19X2 and 19Xl

	19X2	19X1
ASSETS		
CURRENT ASSETS		
Cash	$ 17,322	$ 1,488
Accounts receivable	31,079	8,623
Inventory-at lower of cost (first-in first-out method) or market	47,187	14,306
Other current assets	582	696
TOTAL CURRENT ASSETS	96,170	25,113
PROPERTY AND EQUIPMENT— on the basis of cost	40,723	25,089
Accumulated depreciation	(18,437)	(13,502)
	22,286	11,587
OTHER ASSETS	4,738	3,535
	$ 123,194	**$ 40235**
LIABILITIES AND PROPRIETOR'S CAPITAL		
CURRENT LIABILITIES		
Current portion of long-term debt	$ 7,840	$ 4,440
Accounts payable	23,936	3,045
Payroll taxes payable	1,830	914
Sales tax payable	2,916	1,701
TOTAL CURRENT LIABILITIES	36,522	10,100
LONG-TERM DEBT, net of current portion	21,892	2,590
PROPRIETOR'S CAPITAL	64,780	27,545
	$ 123,194	**$ 40235**

See accompanying notes and accountant's report.

A. B. JOHNSON COMPANY
STATEMENTS OF INCOME AND PROPRIETOR'S CAPITAL
Years Ended December 31, 19X2 and 19X1

	19X2	19X1
SALES	$ 285,723	$ 174,104
COST OF SALES		
Beginning inventory	14,306	11,292
Purchases	134,367	65,458
Less ending inventory	(47,187)	(14,3)
	101,486	62,444
GROSS PROFIT	184,237	111,660
EXPENSES		
Salaries	54,774	49,387
Sales tax	12,182	9,285
Utilities	9,019	8,081
Rent	8,002	7,075
Auto and truck	5,743	3,653
Depreciation	4,935	3,341
Payroll tax	4,915	3,195
Insurance	4,322	2,987
Office	1,933	1,163
Legal and professional	2,790	1,029
Freight	1,730	962
Advertising	900	774
Maintenance and repair	1,315	724
Interest	778	358
Property tax	300	224
Dues and subscriptions	225	190
Commissions and contracts	800	175
Exempt salaries	-	174
Entertainment and promotion	732	113
Auto licenses	142	75
Equipment rental	743	16
	116,280	92,981
NET INCOME	67,957	18,679
PROPRIETOR'S CAPITAL AT BEGINNING OF YEAR	27,545	28,181
Withdrawals	(30,722)	(19,315)
PROPRIETOR'S CAPITAL AT END OF YEAR	$ 64,780	$ 27,545

See accompanying notes and accountant's report.

A. B. JOHNSON COMPANY
STATEMENTS OF CASH FLOWS
Years Ended December 31, 19X2 and 19Xl

	19X2	19X1
CASH FLOWS FROM OPERATING ACTIVITIES		
Net income	$ 67,957	$ 18,679
Adjustments to reconcile net income to net cash		
provided by operating activities:		
Depreciation	4,935	3,341
Increase in sales tax payable	1,215	1,701
(Increase) decrease in accounts receivable	(22,456)	4,040
(Increase) decrease in inventory	(32,881)	(3,014)
(Increase) decrease in other current assets	114	(614)
Increase (decrease) in accounts payable	20,891	(4,895)
Increase (decrease) in payroll taxes payable	916	(133)
NET CASH PROVIDED BY OPERATING ACTIVITIES	40,691	19,105
CASH FLOWS FROM INVESTING ACTIVITIES		
Purchases of property and equipment	(15,634)	(10,291)
Purchases of other assets	(1,203)	—
NET CASH USED BY INVESTING ACTIVITIES	(16,837)	(10,291)
CASH FLOWS FROM FINANCING ACTIVITIES		
Proceeds from issuance of long-term debt	27,142	7,030
Repayments on long-term debt	(4,440)	—
Repayments on note payable	—	(702)
Withdrawals by proprietor	(30,722)	(19,315)
NET CASH USED BY FINANCING ACTIVITIES	(8,020)	(12,987)
NET INCREASE (DECREASE) IN CASH	15,834	(4,173)
CASH AT BEGINNING OF YEAR	1,488	5,661
CASH AT END OF YEAR	$ 17,322	$ 1,488

See accompanying notes and accountant's report.

A. B. JOHNSON COMPANY
NOTES TO FINANCIAL STATEMENTS
December 31, 19X2 and 19X1[1]

NOTE A — SUMMARY OF SIGNIFICANT ACCOUNTING POLICIES

Nature of Operations and Basis of Accounting

A. B. Johnson Company, a proprietorship, is engaged in the custom draperies business with one store located in Houston, Texas. The Company's financial statements are presented in accordance with generally accepted accounting principles. The accompanying financial statements have been prepared solely from the accounts of A.B. Johnson Company, and the owner represents that they do not include his personal accounts or those of any other operation in which he is engaged.

Property and Equipment

Depreciation of property and equipment is provided on both the straight-line and declining-balance methods. Expenditures for maintenance and repairs are charged against operations. Renewals and betterments that materially extend the life of the asset are capitalized.

Revenue Recognition

Layaway sales are not reported as income until final payment is received and the merchandise is delivered.

Income Taxes

The proprietorship itself is not a taxpaying entity for purposes of federal and state income taxes. Federal and state income taxes of the proprietor are computed on his total income from all sources; accordingly, no provision for income taxes is made in these statements. The proprietor customarily makes estimated tax payments toward his personal income tax liability from the proprietorship bank account. These payments are treated as withdrawals of capital. Subsequent to December 31, 19X2, the proprietor withdrew $5,000 from the proprietorship for the purpose of making his fourth and final estimated tax payment for 19X2.

Use of Estimates

The preparation of financial statements in conformity with generally accepted accounting principles requires the proprietor to make estimates and assumptions that affect certain reported amounts and disclosures. Accordingly, actual results could differ from those estimates.

---

[1]Notes relate to the accompanying statements, each of which is dated. In practice, some firms include the balance sheet date in the caption while others do not.

NOTE B — LONG-TERM DEBT

Long-term debt consisted of the following notes payable to banks:

19X2 19X1

Note payable to North National Bank, payable in 24 equal monthly installments of $428 (including interest at 10 percent), collateralized by an automobile with a net book value of $3,135 at December 31, 19X2	$ 2,590	$ 7,030
Note payable to GIC, Inc., payable in 48 equal monthly installments of $775 (including interest at 14.5 percent), collateralized by equipment with a net book value of $31,275 at December 31, 19X2	27,142	—
	29,732	7,030
Less current portion	(7,840)	(4,440)
	$ 21,892	**$ 2,590**

Cash payments for interest on these notes was $675 and $326 for the years ended December 31, 19X2 and 19X1, respectively.[2]

Maturities of long-term debt are as follows:

Year Ending December 31	Amount
19X3	$ 7,840
19X4	6,730
19X5	7,561
19X6	7,601
	$ 29,732

The fair value of the Company's long-term debt is estimated based on current rates offered to the Company for debt of the same remaining maturities. At December 31, 19X2, the carrying amount of long-term debt approximates fair value.[3]

NOTE C — COMMITMENTS

The Company leases its store facilities under a five-year operating lease for $670 per month. The lease has a renewal option of two additional five-year periods. The remaining lease commitment over the primary five-year term of the lease (which expires December 31, 19X4) is $32,200. The lease agreement also provides for an escalation in yearly lease expense equal to 14 percent of the excess of annual sales over $300,000.

[2] According to SFAS No. 95, Statement of Cash Flows, when the indirect method of reporting cash flow from operating activities is used, the amount of interest paid (net of amounts capitalized) must be disclosed.

[3] The portion of this note relating to the fair value of financial instruments is an optional disclosure due to the issuance of SFAS No. 126, Exemption from Certain Required Disclosures about Financial Instruments for Certain Nonpublic Entities: An Amendment of SFAS No. 107. SFAS No. 126, which is effective for fiscal years ending after December 15, 1996, makes SFAS No. 107's disclosures about the fair value of financial instruments optional for companies that meet certain criteria. Those criteria are listed at Appendix 5B-19. (For fiscal years beginning after June 15, 2000, SFAS No. 133, Accounting for Derivative Instruments and Hedging Activities, revises SFAS No. 126's criteria for optional disclosure about the fair value of financial instruments. Those revised criteria are listed at Appendix 5B-19.)

APPENDIX B

PARTNERSHIP —
COMPILED, ACCRUAL BASIS,
FULL DISCLOSURE

JOINT VENTURE, LTD.

FINANCIAL STATEMENTS

Year Ended December 31, 19XI

To the Partners
Joint Venture, Ltd.
Fort Worth, Texas

We have compiled the accompanying balance sheet of Joint Venture, Ltd. (a limited partnership) as of December 31, 19X1, and the related statements of operations and partners' capital and cash flows for the year then ended, in accordance with Statements on Standards for Accounting and Review Services issued by the American Institute of Certified Public Accountants.

A compilation is limited to presenting in the form of financial statements information that is the representation of management. We have not audited or reviewed the accompanying financial statements and, accordingly, do not express an opinion or any other form of assurance on them.

(Firm's signature)

February 15, 19X2

JOINT VENTURE, LTD.
BALANCE SHEET
December 31, 19Xl

ASSETS

CURRENT ASSETS		
Cash		$ 217,475
Accounts receivable, net of allowance for doubtful accounts of $4,000		40,342
TOTAL CURRENT ASSETS		257,817

OIL AND GAS PROPERTIES		
Developed properties, including intangible development costs		1,293,833
Lease and well equipment		850,984
		2,144,017
Accumulated depreciation		(39,406)
Amortization of costs of developed properties		(135,693)
		1,969,718
		$ 2,227,535

LIABILITIES AND PARTNERS' CAPITAL

CURRENT LIABILITIES		
Current maturities of long-term debt		$ 335,605
Accounts payable		192,267
Accrued interest		51,367
TOTAL CURRENT LIABILITIES		579,239
LONG-TERM DEBT, net of current maturities		1,059,363
PARTNERS' CAPITAL		588,933
		$ 2,227,535

See accompanying notes and accountants' report.

JOINT VENTURE, LTD.
STATEMENT OF OPERATIONS AND PARTNERS' CAPITAL
Year Ended December 31, 19XI

OIL AND GAS SALES	$ 263,938
PRODUCTION COSTS	
Lease operating expenses	45,011
Taxes on production and property	38,272
Depreciation	39,406
Amortization of costs of developed properties	135,693
	258,382
EXPLORATION COSTS (Dry hole costs)	288,000
GENERAL AND ADMINISTRATIVE EXPENSES	
Legal and professional	1,450
Other	3,693
	5,143
INTEREST EXPENSE	116,623
NET LOSS	(404,210)
PARTNERS' CAPITAL AT BEGINNING OF YEAR	764,197
Capital contributions	228,946
PARTNERS' CAPITAL AT END OF YEAR	**$ 588,933**

See accompanying notes and accountants' report.

JOINT VENTURE, LTD.
STATEMENT OF CASH FLOWS
Year Ended December 31, 19Xl

CASH FLOWS FROM OPERATING ACTIVITIES	
Net loss	$ (404,210)
Adjustments to reconcile net income to net cash used by operations	
Depreciation	39,406
Amortization of costs of developed properties	135,693
Increase in accounts receivable	(40,342)
Increase in accounts payable	190,267
Increase in accrued interest	27,799
NET CASH USED BY OPERATING ACTIVITIES	(51,387)
CASH FLOWS FROM INVESTING ACTIVITIES	
Additions to developed oil and gas properties	(192,000)
Purchases of lease and well equipment	(184,509)
NET CASH USED BY INVESTING ACTIVITIES	(376,509)
CASH FLOWS FROM FINANCING ACTIVITIES	
Additions to long-term debt	403,464
Repayments on long-term debt	(268,496)
Capital contributions	228,946
NET CASH PROVIDED BY FINANCING ACTIVITIES	363,914
NET DECREASE IN CASH	(63,982)
CASH AT BEGINNING OF YEAR	281,457
CASH AT END OF YEAR	$ 217,475

See accompanying notes and accountants' report.

JOINT VENTURE, LTD.
NOTES TO FINANCIAL STATEMENTS
December 31, 19X1[1]

NOTE A — SUMMARY OF SIGNIFICANT ACCOUNTING POLICIES

Nature of Operations

The partnership is engaged in the exploration and drilling of oil wells, primarily in the Permian Basin area of West Texas.

Developed Properties

The partnership capitalizes all leasehold and intangible drilling costs for productive wells and amortizes these costs to expense using the units of production method. Costs related to nonproductive wells are charged to expense at the time a well is determined to be nonproductive. A summary of developed property costs follows:

Property acquisition costs	$ 306,000
Development costs	987,833
	$ 1,293,833

Lease and Well Equipment

The cost of lease and well equipment is charged to expense through depreciation, using the units of production method for each respective well.

Income Taxes

All tax effects of the partnership's income or loss are passed through to the partners individually. For tax purposes, all intangible drilling and development costs and advanced royalties are expensed when incurred. Lease and well equipment is depreciated using the accelerated cost recovery system rates.

Use of Estimates

The preparation of financial statements in conformity with generally accepted accounting principles requires the partners to make estimates and assumptions that affect certain reported amounts and disclosures. Accordingly, actual results could differ from those estimates.

---

[1] In practice, some firms include the balance sheet date in the caption, while others do not.

NOTE B — LONG-TERM DEBT

At December 31, 19X1, long-term debt, collateralized by substantially all the assets of the partnership, consisted of the following:

Note payable to St. John Exploration Company, payable $21,604 monthly, including interest at 9 percent per annum.	$ 798,718
Note payable to St. John Exploration Company, payable $4,982 monthly, including interest at 9 percent per annum.	240,000
Notes payable to Commerce Bank, payable $9,375 monthly, plus interest at 2 percent over prime with a maximum of 15 percent per annum.	356,250
	1,394,968
Less current maturities	(335,605)
	$ 1,059,363

Maturities of long-term debt are as follows:

Year Ending December 31,	Amount
19X2	$ 335,605
19X3	275,415
19X4	260,108
19X5	204,729
19X6	192,604
Thereafter	126,507
	$ 1,394,968

During the year ended December 31, 19X1, the partnership's interest payments totaled $88,824.[2]

The fair value of the partnership's long-term debt is estimated based on current rates offered to the partnership for debt of the same remaining maturities. At December 31, 19X1, the fair value of the long-term debt approximates the amounts recorded in the financial statements.

NOTE C — COMMITMENTS

In accordance with the partnership agreement, the general partner, with the approval of a majority of the limited partners, contracted to drill three additional wells for a turnkey price of $480,000. One limited partner, representing a 19 percent interest, declined participation in the new program and will be excluded from income participation related to these three wells until the fulfillment of the recoupment provisions as contained in the partnership agreement.

---

[2] Under SFAS No. 95, Statements of Cash Flows, if the indirect method is used to report cash provided by operating activities, cash payments for interest should be separately disclosed. See Section 508 for a discussion of SFAS No. 95.

Index

Acres U.S.A. —
books are just the beginning!

Farmers around the world are learning to grow bountiful crops profitably — without risking their own health and destroying the fertility of the soil. *Acres U.S.A.* can show you how. If you want to be on the cutting edge of eco-farming technologies, techniques, markets, news, analysis and trends, look to *Acres U.S.A.*

For over 30 years, we've been the independent voice for eco-agriculture. Each oversized monthly issue is packed with practical, hands-on information you can put to work on your farm, bringing solutions to your most pressing problems. Get the advice consultants charge thousands for . . .

- Fertility management
- Non-chemical weed & insect control
- Specialty crops & marketing
- Grazing, composting, natural veterinary care
- Soil's link to human & animal health

For a free sample copy or to subscribe, visit us online at
www.acresusa.com
or call toll-free in the U.S. and Canada
800-355-5313
Outside U.S. & Canada call (512) 892-4400
24-hour fax (512) 892-4448
info@acresusa.com